Buying local is a subject I've been
time now – and I can tell you I'm
about it anytime soon. Sourcing f
and processed as close to home a
far-reaching commitments a sho
about reducing your carbon foot
local businesses, though these ar

locally. Perhaps what matters most is that exploring and supporting your local food network will enrich the very culture you find yourself living in. It strengthens communities, keeps traditions alive, enhances the landscape and brings a better understanding and appreciation of the food you eat.

The message in this year's River Cottage diary – buy local, buy seasonal – may be one you've heard before. But take a fresh look around your own area and you may be amazed by how much is new. The local food scene in this country has never been more vibrant or dynamic. If you want confirmation of that, check out the multitude of food festivals that are burgeoning in every area in every season – from the South-west's Great British Cheese Festival (27th/28th September) to Kent's Cherry Day (20th July) or the Conwy Honey Fair (13th September). These events couldn't take place without passionate producers and equally passionate consumers. Countless farmers, growers and cooks are changing their focus from large-scale, industrialised, anonymous food to hand-produced, locally sourced fare. They're doing this because we, the shoppers, want them too. Things really are changing – small decisions taken at a local level make a huge difference.

As well as 36 delicious seasonal recipes, information on regional food producers and food events, and helpful stats on everything from game seasons to grams and ounces, you'll find a section of this year's diary devoted to one particular local food venture that's very close to my heart. Establishing the River Cottage Store has shown me at first hand the trials, tests and incredible rewards to be had from taking a local approach to food. I hope lots of you will be able to visit us in Axminster in the coming year. Not least to see, and taste, what wonderful food our own local heroes are producing.

Enjoy 2008.

Hugh

The River Cottage Axminster Store

If you'd asked me early in 2007 what I thought about the South-west's local food producers, I would have waxed lyrical for sure. 'It's great down here,' I would have said, 'there are so many talented farmers, growers and craftspeople on our doorstep.' Now, a year later, with the River Cottage Axminster Store up and running, that sounds like faint praise. I knew things were good around here – but this good? It's an embarrassment of riches – though I've never quite understood that phrase, as we are mightily proud of and not the least bit embarrassed by what we are offering.

The idea of opening a River Cottage Store was compelling for several reasons: for a start, it seemed like a natural extension of our HQ at Park Farm, where we run all kinds of courses, all based around the ideal of getting ever closer to the source of the food we eat. We grow a lot of fresh produce and raise our own livestock, most of which goes directly to the River Cottage kitchen to feed guests at our events, but we also rely on a whole network of regional producers to supply us with the things that we can't always produce ourselves, like beer and cheese. We've long felt inspired by what we knew the South-west had to offer, and increasingly felt confident that there was enough sheer excellence around us to fill a shop. At the same time, we relished the challenge of running a commercially viable business while sticking to the principles of selling local, seasonal food, and taking sustainability into account every step of the way – from the recycled apple crates the shelves are made of to the eco-friendly paint on the walls.

By February 2007 we'd found a fantastic building, the New Commercial Inn in the heart of Axminster (just a few miles from Park Farm), and began honing our vision of a thriving store selling the very best in local fresh fruit and veg, meat and bread, pickles and preserves, butter and cheese, wine and beer. We also decided we wanted the shop to have an informal, easy-going restaurant, or 'canteen', where shoppers and their families could stop for anything from a cup of tea and a slice of cake to a full three-course meal. And we decided, with characteristic optimism (some might say, with pie-in-the-sky wishful thinking), that we'd like to open by the summer – to give our first customers a taste of Devon and Dorset's finest fresh fruit and vegetables at the very peak of the growing season. It was a huge challenge. There were a lot of late-night meetings, working weekends and the occasional heated discussion – but we did it! (Well, we were a bit late with our fully fledged grand opening, but we were selling fabulous local fruit and veg by the start of July.)

That is in no small part down to the efforts of our fantastic retail manager, Anna Woodrow, and her plucky assistant, Pip Corbin. Together, they travelled all over the region – taking in Cornwall, Devon, Dorset, Somerset, Wiltshire and Gloucestershire – tasting, testing and talking. They sampled everything from obscure varieties of Cornish plum to organic trout raised on the watercress beds of Wiltshire. Back at River Cottage HQ they had to run the gauntlet of a second panel of tasters – myself, and pretty much the entire River Cottage team. How they coped with so much input, and so much 'lively debate', I'll never know. I recall one memorable exchange: 'That jam's amazing!' 'No it's not. It's rank!' 'That's because you just tasted it with the mustard spoon.' And the discussions haven't stopped. We are constantly reviewing and revising our range. And now we have the most important taste panel to help us do that – our customers.

Of course we encountered problems along the way. It took us months to track down a supply of organic beef that really cut the mustard. But the beautiful Devon ruby red meat we're now getting from Rod & Ben's, near Exeter, was well worth the wait. We despaired of ever finding a locally made range of charcuterie, until we stumbled on the wonderful artisan products of Grahame and Simon at Trealy Farm. On occasion we are prepared to depart from our strict local brief to celebrate some regional British products that are quite simply inimitable. From Scotland, for example, we have an organic single malt from Speyside, and amazing oatcakes. And yes, we do sell bananas – but they're organic and fair trade, and we know, week by week, exactly which farms they come from.

Our hope has always been to help make Axminster *the* local food town of our region. But we are well aware that a number of independent food shops in the town were making a fantastic contribution to the local food culture long before we set our sights on the New Commercial Inn. Ganesha Wholefoods were well known to us as we have long relied on their outstanding range of organic grains and pulses, flours, dried fruits, spices and culinary oils in the kitchen at Park Farm. MacSarson's, the Axminster fishmonger, Complete Meats, the excellent local butcher, Punch and Judy, the bakery, and the fabulous Miller's farm shop (just outside town on the A35) are all family businesses deeply committed to local sourcing. And the sweet shop next door to us is a treasure trove for the sugary-toothed.

If you come to Axminster to see us, you'll reap great rewards from visiting these stores too. In one sense they are our competition – and that's how it should be, since local food economies thrive on genuine local choice. But they are also, we feel, our partners, in an on-going mission to provide a sustainable, local, ethical and, perhaps above all, passionate alternative to the industrially produced supermarket foods that aim to dominate the modern market.

In the end it's the public themselves, the people of Axminster and beyond, who hold the key, not only to our success but to that of local food culture as a whole. They have patiently watched the edifice of their old Commercial Inn slowly transformed into the River Cottage Store. And ever since we opened, their positive comments, helpful suggestions, all round goodwill and, of course, their custom have been crucial to our success.

So, thank you, Axminster, East Devon and West Dorset, and all who have come from further afield. We hope to go on feeding you, and your families, with the very best local food, throughout the seasons, for many years to come.

Thanks also to all our fantastic local producers. You can find out more about some of them on the pages that follow.

Mark Diacono and Otter Farm

Environmental consultant Mark Diacono believes that, with our changing climate, we should be considering growing foods more usually found in the Mediterranean. At his 'climate change farm', an end-of-terrace house just outside Honiton, he's turning 17 acres of former county council farmland into a modern day Eden. Mark started by creating a list of all the fresh produce he liked, then crossed out the most exotic foods and those that were already locally grown. He was left with a roll call of forgotten English favourites such as mulberries, medlars, quinces and sorbs (sour fruits, a little bit like crab apples), as well as foods more usually found in places like the south of France or Tuscany, including olives, almonds, pecans, persimmons, apricots and peaches. Mark practises a principle called forest gardening, which relies on companion planting as a low-impact, high-output way of producing food. The farm is divided into different 'rooms', each with its own mini eco-system, and each plant complements its fellows. So, for example, his peach orchard is under-planted with white and crimson clover, which fixes nitrogen in the soil. He grows herbs to keep pests away and uses hedges of harvestable walnut, small-leafed lime and Canadian allspice as windbreaks. Mark sees this middle ground between farming and gardening as an exciting and highly productive new approach. 'It enables us to take advantage of warmer conditions,' he explains, 'but, at the same time, reduce the threat of future climate change: growing foods that would otherwise be imported is a good way to shrink our carbon footprint.'

Find out how Mark is doing – follow his blog at www.otterfarm.co.uk.

Thyme after Time, locally sourced preserves

Thyme after Time, based in the heart of the Blackmore Vale, is the culmination of Margot Eavis's dreams. She was looking for a new outlet for her culinary talents that would allow her to stay at home to look after her young son. Realising that there was a wealth of fresh fruit, herbs and vegetables available locally, she decided that making preserves that used up gluts of this seasonal produce was the perfect solution. The work was easy to do in small batches in her kitchen, and her products had a long shelf life. She now takes advantage of every preserving opportunity that comes along, dreaming up simple combinations of seasonal ingredients that taste wonderful and look amazing too. Her claret-coloured pear and tarragon jelly (a favourite of Hugh's) is a case in point. Margot has built up a network of small local suppliers who let her know when a glut is imminent, at which point she swings into action. She might find herself turning fruit from the local cider orchard into apple and walnut jelly, using runner beans from a local allotment to create a rich pickle, or gathering elderflowers from a nearby field for gooseberry and elderflower jelly. Margot is particularly proud of her Seasonal Limited Editions, which include delights such as Dorset pickled asparagus. 'This lovely vegetable has such a short season,' she says, 'and I really wanted to capture its essence in a jar. I knew the Victorians pickled their asparagus so I developed my own recipe, taking it a step further by adding lemon and tarragon.' With a true gift for combining flavours, Margot ensures that no glut is ever wasted.

Brown Cow Organics, makers of River Cottage Yoghurt

When the price of organic milk began to plummet in 2003, dairy farmers Judith and Clive Freane of Pilton, in Somerset, realised they needed to find new ways to use the milk their herd was producing. Judith felt that making yoghurt would be a good way to diversify, and so her new enterprise began. An opportune knock on the door from Hugh led to a conversation round the kitchen table and subsequently to the birth of a River Cottage brand of live organic Guernsey yoghurts. It's easy to see why Hugh was so impressed: the rich milk from the Freanes' Guernseys produces an exceptionally smooth, rich and creamy yoghurt. Judith and Clive believe that to produce great-tasting milk, you have to start at grass roots. A soil nutrition expert analyses each field for minerals and trace elements to assess its health status. Then Judith's brother, who is a vet, analyses the grass and fodder fed to the animals. Any imbalances are corrected using organically approved supplements. This close attention to detail results in an extremely healthy, happy herd of cows that produce milk rich in nutrients and high in omega-3 fats. Judith and her helpers, Alison and Debbie, carefully make 3,000 pots of yoghurt a week, gently hand-whisking it to keep it thick and velvety, before pouring it into recyclable glass jars. 'Why waste money on vitamin and mineral supplements,' says Judith, 'when something better can be found in the food that you eat?'

Brown and Forrest, artisan smokers

This small family business started back in the early 1980s, hot-smoking local eels in a converted cider barn. At that time there was no history of smoking eel in Somerset, so it took a lot of local leg work and blind-tastings to win over a suspicious public. Now, however, smoked eel is Brown and Forrest's biggest seller. Owner Jesse Pattison buys his eels from rivermen on the Test, Stour, Avon and Piddle. He also ensures that they restock the rivers each year with young eels bought from the Bristol Channel fisheries. The eels are hot-smoked by master smoker Steve Taylor, who hangs the brined fish over open fires for 15 minutes before damping down the flames with beech chippings and apple twigs so the eels can gently smoke for two hours. Alongside their hot-smoker, Brown and Forrest have two 6-foot, square, brick cold-smokers, where they cure salmon, large trout, cheeses, haddock and garlic for 18–20 hours, over slow-burning oak dust. All the sawdust and chippings are by-products from furniture makers and sawmills in the Somerset levels. Jesse has recently started to source local, hand-line-caught fish from Brixham, including mackerel, which is hot-smoked, and bass and pollack, which are cold-smoked.

Five Penny Farm, a sustainable co-operative smallholding

Five Penny Farm is an organic smallholding run by Jyoti Fernandes, husband Dai and friends Kerry and Olly. Five years ago these two families moved from Tinkers Bubble, an eco-community in Somerset, to set up their own co-operative on 43 acres of land at Wootton Fitzpaine, near Bridport. They built timber and straw bale houses and live a low-impact, sustainable life using compost toilets and power from solar panels and a couple of small windmills. The group's aim was to establish a centre that other local smallholders could use, so they built a central thatched barn, which has become a community processing centre. It's divided into various processing rooms that can be hired out, including a dairy, a cutting room for meat, a jam-making room, a juice press and a herb dryer. Five Penny Farm has its own market stall in Bridport every Saturday, where much of its produce is sold. The farm functions well, says Jyoti, because they have a little bit of everything, all working together. So the sheep graze in the orchard, the pigs turn over the root vegetable plot once it has been harvested, and the chickens scratch around the veg patch for grubs and insects. Jyoti hopes this model of a community co-op that brings like-minded smallholders together will inspire others to follow in their wake.

The Town Mill Bakery, Lyme Regis

When he couldn't find any good bread for his restaurant in Lyme Regis, Clive Cobb thought it was high time the town had its own bakery. Aidan Chapman, a master baker of great renown who was working in Bridport at the time, was looking for pastures new, and Clive was able to persuade him to join his new venture. From its launch in August 2005, The Town Mill Bakery in Coombe Street has been a phenomenal success. Within a few years, Clive and Aidan moved the bakery to the more spacious surroundings of a 600-year-old mill in the heart of town. Aidan starts baking at 8am, and everything is made from scratch using as many local ingredients as possible. That includes organic flour from Shaftesbury and Devon buffalo mozzarella for the pizzas. Many of The Town Mill Bakery's breads use a sourdough starter – a living culture of wild yeasts found in the air – which Aidan lovingly nurtures and feeds daily. He believes using this culture makes for a more intense flavour in the bread. This passion for using only the best ingredients has made Clive and Aidan's project a thriving success in the heart of Lyme.

Sydling Brook Organic Farm

Always passionate about the countryside and its diversity, Alastair
Cooper finally took the plunge seven years ago and left his job in the city
to become a farmer. After a year at agricultural college, he moved to West
Dorset and bought Sydling Brook Farm, 2,500 acres of chalk downland,
water meadow and pasture. His first step was to make the entire farm
organic. At the time, many thought him mad, but now four neighbouring
farms have converted too and Sydling Valley is the largest area of
organic lowland in England. With the support of his team, including
head stockman Andy Elford (pictured), Alastair uses traditional mixed
farming methods, rotating crops, leaving margins on the fields as wildlife
habitat and raising traditional breeds of animal. He put a lot of research
into finding the ideal free-range chicken, finally settling on a French
breed called Sasso. Developed from an old English variety, it is slow-
growing, with dense meat and a good flavour. The organic chicks arrive at
Sydling Brook Farm at just a day old. From the outset, they have access
to paddocks of lush grass and clover as well as organic grain from the
farm. They live in very small flocks of 180 birds, and at 12–16 weeks they
are ready to go to the on-site abattoir (the average commercial bird is
slaughtered at just over five weeks). Alastair and Andy believe that small
flocks, early access to a truly free-range lifestyle and time to grow makes
for an excellent chicken. They're not the only ones to think so: Sydling
Brook Farm's chickens won gold at the Organic Food Awards last year.

Toby Roskilly and Roskilly's Ice Cream

In 1987 the Roskilly family realised their dairy farm had to diversify in order to survive. Deciding to give ice cream-making a go, they spent the summer experimenting, turning milk and cream from their herd of Jersey cows into ice cream with some truly unusual flavours. Mum Rachel had always been a fabulous pudding-maker, so they created ice cream versions of many of her recipes: sherry trifle, banoffee pie, flapjack and hokey pokey to name but a few. By the end of the summer they had 25 flavours under their belt. Unable to decide which ones to use commercially, the Roskillys put up posters advertising a free taste test. The following morning, 250 people turned up at their remote Cornish farm. Boosted by this success, they carried on creating new flavours, and haven't stopped yet. Rachel's son Toby is keen to experiment with new combinations: his avocado and garlic ice cream may not have worked (it oxidised and turned black) but his yoghurt-based raita ice is a big hit. Toby believes that you should be able to blind-taste an ice cream and know immediately what flavour it is. These days, the Roskillys produce ice cream in 42 flavours. Toby is trying to curb his enthusiasm, limiting their repertoire to 22 regular flavours with a rolling menu of 6 limited editions, but he finds it hard work. 'I'm working on a whisky and black pepper ice at the moment,' he admits.

Personal notes

Name

Home address

Telephone

Fax

Mobile

Email

Work address

Telephone

Fax

Mobile

Email

Emergency contact

Address

Telephone

Fax

Mobile

Email

Conversion charts

Useful measurements

Measurement	Imperial	Metric
1 American cup	8fl oz	225ml
1 egg, size 3	2fl oz	56ml
1 egg white	1fl oz	28ml
1 rounded tablespoon flour	1oz	30g
1 rounded tablespoon cornflour	1oz	30g
1 rounded tablespoon caster sugar	1oz	30g
2 rounded tablespoons fresh breadcrumbs	1oz	30g
2 level teaspoons gelatine	1/4oz	8g
1 American tablespoon of butter	1/2oz	15g
packet granular aspic	1oz sets 1 pint liquid	30g sets 570ml liquid
three leaves powdered gelatine	1/2oz sets 1 pint liquid	15g sets 570ml liquid

Weights

Imperial	Metric
1/4oz	7–8g
1/2oz	15g
3/4oz	20g
1oz	30g
2oz	55g
3oz	85g
4oz (1/4lb)	110g
5oz	140g
6oz	170g
7oz	200g
8oz (1/2lb)	225g
9oz	255g
10oz	285g
11oz	310g
12oz (3/4lb)	340g
13oz	370g
14oz	400g
15oz	425g
16oz (1lb)	450g
1 1/4lb	560g
1 1/2lb	675g
2lb	900g
3lb	1.35kg
4lb	1.80kg
5lb	2.30kg
6lb	2.70kg
7lb	3.20kg
8lb	3.60kg
9lb	4.00kg
10lb	4.50kg

Lengths

Imperial	Metric
1/16in	2mm
1/12in	3mm
1/6in	4mm
1/4in	6mm
1/2in	1cm
3/4in	2cm
1in	2.5cm
1 1/4in	3cm
1 1/2in	4cm
1 3/4in	4.5cm
2in	5cm
2 1/2in	6cm
3in	7.5cm
3 1/2in	9cm
4in	10cm
5in	13cm
5 1/4in	13.5cm
6in	15cm
6 1/2in	16cm
7in	18cm
7 1/2in	19cm
8in	20cm
9in	23cm
9 1/2in	24cm
10in	25.5cm
11in	28cm
12in	30cm
13in	32.5cm
14in	35cm
16in	40cm

Volumes

Imperial	Metric
1 tsp	5ml
2 tbsp	28ml
4 tbsp	56ml
2fl oz	55ml
3fl oz	75ml
5fl oz (1/4 pint)	150ml
6.6fl oz (1/3 pint)	190ml
10fl oz (1/2 pint)	290ml
15fl oz (3/4 pint)	425ml
20fl oz (1 pint)	570ml
35fl oz (1 3/4 pints)	1 litre

Wine quantities

	fl oz	ml
1 glass liqueur	1	45
1 glass port/sherry	2	70
1 glass wine	3	100
Average wine bottle	25	750

Oven temperatures

°C	°F	Gas
140	275	1
150	300	2
170	325	3
180	350	4
190	375	5
200	400	6
220	425	7
230	450	8
240	475	9

For fan-assisted ovens reduce temperature by 20°C

Shooting seasons

Game and wild fowl

Coot	1 Sept–31 Jan
Duck and goose	
inland Eng, Scot, Wales	1 Sept–31 Jan
foreshore Eng, Scot, Wales	1 Sept–20 Feb
N. Ireland	1 Sept–31 Jan
Golden plover	1 Sept–31 Jan
Grouse	
Eng, Scot, Wales	12 Aug–10 Dec
N. Ireland	12 Aug–30 Nov
Hare	
Eng, Scot, Wales	1 Aug–29 Feb
N. Ireland	12 Aug–31 Jan
Moorhen	1 Sept–31 Jan
Partridge	1 Sept–1 Feb
Pheasant	
Eng, Scot, Wales	1 Oct–1 Feb
N. Ireland (cocks only)	1 Oct–31 Jan
Rabbit	No closed season
Common snipe	
Eng, Scot, Wales	12 Aug–31 Jan
N. Ireland	1 Sept–31 Jan
Jack snipe (N. Ireland only)	1 Sept–31 Jan
Woodcock	
Eng, Wales	1 Oct–31 Jan
Scot	1 Sept–31 Jan
Wood pigeon	No closed season

Deer

Fallow buck	1 Aug–30 Apr
Fallow doe	
Eng, Wales, N. Ireland	1 Nov–28 Feb
Scot	21 Oct–15 Feb
Red deer stag	
Eng, Wales, N. Ireland	1 Aug–30 Apr
Scot	1 July–20 Oct
Red deer hind	
Eng, Wales, N. Ireland	1 Nov–28 Feb
Scot	21 Oct–15 Feb
Roe buck	
Eng, Wales	1 Apr–31 Oct
Scot	1 Apr–20 Oct
Roe doe	
Eng, Wales	1 Nov–28 Feb
Scot	21 Oct–31 Mar
Sika stag	
Eng, Wales, N. Ireland	1 Aug–30 Apr
Scot	1 July–20 Oct
Sika hind	
Eng, Wales, N. Ireland	1 Nov–28 Feb
Scot	21 Oct–15 Feb

Landing sizes

Bass	360mm
Brill	300mm
Clam	40mm
Razor clam	100mm
Cockles	23mm
Cod	350mm
Conger eel	580mm
Brown crab	140mm
Spider crab	
female	120mm
male	130mm
Velvet crab	65mm
Crawfish	110mm
Dab	230mm
Flounder	270mm
Haddock	300mm
Hake	270mm
Herring	200mm
Lemon sole	250mm
Ling	630mm
Blue ling	700mm
Lobster	87mm
Mackerel	300mm
Megrim	200mm
Grey mullet	300mm
Red mullet	150mm
Mussel	50mm
Oyster	70mm
Plaice	270mm
Pollack	300mm
Saithe	350mm
Sardine	110mm
Horse mackerel scad	250mm
Scallop	110mm
Queen scallop	40mm
Black sea bream	230mm
Red sea bream	250mm
Whole skate	400mm
Wing skate	200mm
Sole	240mm
Turbot	300mm
Whelk	45mm
Whiting	270mm

These charts are to be used as a guide and should not be used as a definitive statement of current regulations.

Sowing and planting times for vegetables

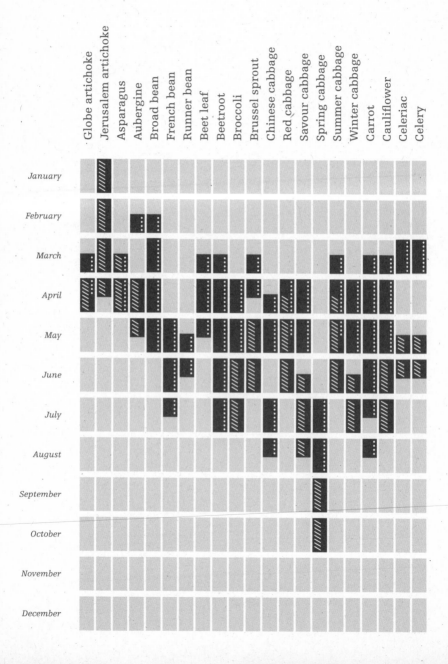

Cucumber

Kale

Leek

Early winter crop lettuce

Spring crop lettuce

Summer crop lettuce

Mangetout and petit pois

Marrow

Onion and shallot from sets

Onion from seed

Parsnip

Pea (June/July crop)

Pea (August crop)

Pea (Autumn Crop)

Asparagus pea

Potato

Radish

Rhubarb

Spinach

Swede

Greenhouse tomato

Plant

Sow

Planting times for fruit

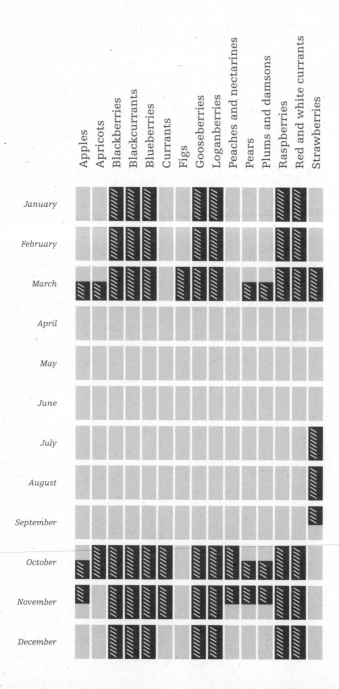

	Apples	Apricots	Blackberries	Blackcurrants	Blueberries	Currants	Figs	Gooseberries	Loganberries	Peaches and nectarines	Pears	Plums and damsons	Raspberries	Red and white currants	Strawberries
January			▨	▨	▨			▨	▨				▨	▨	
February			▨	▨	▨			▨					▨	▨	
March	▨	▨	▨	▨	▨		▨	▨			▨	▨	▨	▨	▨
April															
May															
June															
July															▨
August															▨
September															▨
October	▨	▨	▨	▨	▨		▨	▨	▨		▨	▨	▨	▨	
November	▨		▨	▨	▨		▨	▨		▨	▨	▨	▨	▨	
December			▨	▨	▨			▨	▨				▨	▨	

Plant ▨

Sowing and planting times for herbs

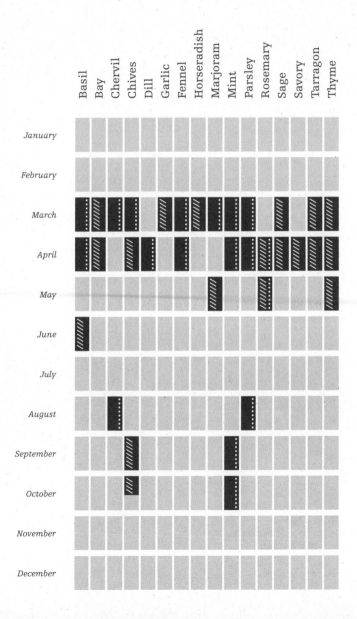

	Basil	Bay	Chervil	Chives	Dill	Garlic	Fennel	Horseradish	Marjoram	Mint	Parsley	Rosemary	Sage	Savory	Tarragon	Thyme
January																
February																
March	Sow	Plant	Sow	Sow		Plant	Sow	Sow	Sow	Sow	Sow		Plant		Sow	Sow
April	Sow	Plant		Sow	Sow		Sow			Sow	Sow	Plant	Plant	Plant	Sow	Sow
May									Plant		Plant					Sow
June	Plant															
July																
August			Sow								Sow					
September				Plant						Sow						
October				Plant						Sow						
November																
December																

Plant Sow

Useful websites

actionaid.org
Action Aid. An agency whose aim is to fight poverty worldwide.

aonb.org.uk
Offers general information about Areas of Outstanding Natural Beauty
(AONBs) in England, Wales and Northern Ireland.

asao.co.uk
Association of Shows and Agricultural Organisations. The full listing of all
agricultural shows across the UK.

basc.org.uk
British Association for Shooting and Conservation. Aims to encourage the
development of country shooting and adherence to codes of practice.

bigbarn.co.uk
A one-stop site where you can find your local food producers and buy direct.

cat.org.uk
Centre for Alternative Technology. Recommends practical solutions to
environmental problems for the twenty-first century.

ciwf.org.uk
Compassion in World Farming. Aims to bring an end to factory farming and
the long-distance transport of animals worldwide.

countrysmallholding.com
Useful information for smallholders, poultry keepers and organic
gardeners. Includes advice on keeping chickens, a breeder's directory and
the opportunity to send questions to qualified vets.

defra.gov.uk
Department for Environment, Food and Rural Affairs. Advice on all
aspects of farming and farm regulations. Cattle registration forms can be
downloaded from the website.

english-nature.org.uk
English Nature. Offers advice and information on the conservation of
wildlife and natural features throughout England.

est.org.uk/myhome
Energy Saving Trust. Find out more about saving energy, money and the
environment in your home.

fairtrade.org.uk
Fairtrade Foundation. Guarantees a better deal for producers in developing
countries. Over 100 products now carry the Fairtrade logo and the website
tells you where to find them, as well as what you can do to support
Fairtrade.

farma.org.uk
National Farmers' Retail & Markets. The largest organization of its type
in the world, representing direct sales to customers through farm
shops, Pick-Your-Own, farmers' markets, home delivery, on-farm catering,
and farm entertainment throughout the UK.

fishing.co.uk
Information about sea and land fishing.

foe.co.uk
Friends of the Earth. International network of environmental pressure groups, with a string of local groups in the UK.

fwag.org.uk
Farming and Wildlife Advisory Group. Exists to provide farmers, landowners and other clients with the best opportunity for environmental gain through cost-effective, quality solutions.

gametoeat.co.uk
Game to Eat. All you need to know about game, including suppliers, recipes and useful links.

gct.org.uk
The Game Conservancy Trust. Promotes the conservation of game in the British countryside and advises on practical management techniques.

greenpeace.org
Greenpeace. Campaigns on environmental issues.

guildofqbutchers.com
Guild of Q Butchers. A useful contact if you are looking for specialist butchers in your area.

metoffice.co.uk
The Met Office. Inshore waters forecast.

rare-breeds.com
Rare Breeds Survival Trust. Charity aiming to conserve Britain's native livestock heritage. Offers details of rare-breed meat suppliers in your area.

regionalfoodanddrink.co.uk
Lists over 3,000 regional food and drink producers in the UK.

rivercottage.net
A website set up to encourage discussion about food, where it comes from and why that matters. Includes edible projects, recipes and recommended producers.

ruralrevival.org.uk
Rural Revival. An action-oriented campaign that aims to break the cycle of rural decline in the UK by supporting the establishment of community and social enterprises. These include community-owned village shops and post offices, recycling services, craft co-operatives, and producer-run farmers' markets.

slowfood.com
Slow Food. An Italian-based international organization of 'eco-gastronomes' wishing to preserve artisan foods and regional traditions.

soilassociation.org
The Soil Association. Offers support and advice on growing and producing organic food.

2008

January

M	T	W	T	F	**S**	**S**
	1	2	3	4	**5**	**6**
7	8	9	10	11	**12**	**13**
14	15	16	17	18	**19**	**20**
21	22	23	24	25	**26**	**27**
28	29	30	31			

February

M	T	W	T	F	**S**	**S**
				1	**2**	**3**
4	5	6	7	8	**9**	**10**
11	12	13	14	15	**16**	**17**
18	19	20	21	22	**23**	**24**
25	26	27	28	29		

March

M	T	W	T	F	**S**	**S**
					1	**2**
3	4	5	6	7	**8**	**9**
10	11	12	13	14	**15**	**16**
17	18	19	20	21	**22**	**23**
24	25	26	27	28	**29**	**30**
31						

April

M	T	W	T	F	**S**	**S**
	1	2	3	4	**5**	**6**
7	8	9	10	11	**12**	**13**
14	15	16	17	18	**19**	**20**
21	22	23	24	25	**26**	**27**
28	29	30				

May

M	T	W	T	F	**S**	**S**
			1	2	**3**	**4**
5	6	7	8	9	**10**	**11**
12	13	14	15	16	**17**	**18**
19	20	21	22	23	**24**	**25**
26	27	28	29	30	**31**	

June

M	T	W	T	F	**S**	**S**
						1
2	3	4	5	6	**7**	**8**
9	10	11	12	13	**14**	**15**
16	17	18	19	20	**21**	**22**
23	24	25	26	27	**28**	**29**
30						

July

M	T	W	T	F	**S**	**S**
	1	2	3	4	**5**	**6**
7	8	9	10	11	**12**	**13**
14	15	16	17	18	**19**	**20**
21	22	23	24	25	**26**	**27**
28	29	30	31			

August

M	T	W	T	F	**S**	**S**
				1	**2**	**3**
4	5	6	7	8	**9**	**10**
11	12	13	14	15	**16**	**17**
18	19	20	21	22	**23**	**24**
25	26	27	28	29	**30**	**31**

September

M	T	W	T	F	**S**	**S**
1	2	3	4	5	**6**	**7**
8	9	10	11	12	**13**	**14**
15	16	17	18	19	**20**	**21**
22	23	24	25	26	**27**	**28**
29	30					

October

M	T	W	T	F	**S**	**S**
		1	2	3	**4**	**5**
6	7	8	9	10	**11**	**12**
13	14	15	16	17	**18**	**19**
20	21	22	23	24	**25**	**26**
27	28	29	30	31		

November

M	T	W	T	F	**S**	**S**
					1	**2**
3	4	5	6	7	**8**	**9**
10	11	12	13	14	**15**	**16**
17	18	19	20	21	**22**	**23**
24	25	26	27	28	**29**	**30**

December

M	T	W	T	F	**S**	**S**
1	2	3	4	5	**6**	**7**
8	9	10	11	12	**13**	**14**
15	16	17	18	19	**20**	**21**
22	23	24	25	26	**27**	**28**
29	30	31				

2009

January

M	T	W	T	F	**S**	**S**
			1	2	**3**	**4**
5	6	7	8	9	**10**	**11**
12	13	14	15	16	**17**	**18**
19	20	21	22	23	**24**	**25**
26	27	28	29	30	**31**	

February

M	T	W	T	F	**S**	**S**
						1
2	3	4	5	6	**7**	**8**
9	10	11	12	13	**14**	**15**
16	17	18	19	20	**21**	**22**
23	24	25	26	27	**28**	

March

M	T	W	T	F	**S**	**S**
						1
2	3	4	5	6	**7**	**8**
9	10	11	12	13	**14**	**15**
16	17	18	19	20	**21**	**22**
23	24	25	26	27	**28**	**29**
30	31					

April

M	T	W	T	F	**S**	**S**
		1	2	3	**4**	**5**
6	7	8	9	10	**11**	**12**
13	14	15	16	17	**18**	**19**
20	21	22	23	24	**25**	**26**
27	28	29	30			

May

M	T	W	T	F	**S**	**S**
				1	**2**	**3**
4	5	6	7	8	**9**	**10**
11	12	13	14	15	**16**	**17**
18	19	20	21	22	**23**	**24**
25	26	27	28	29	**30**	**31**

June

M	T	W	T	F	**S**	**S**
1	2	3	4	5	**6**	**7**
8	9	10	11	12	**13**	**14**
15	16	17	18	19	**20**	**21**
22	23	24	25	26	**27**	**28**
29	30					

July

M	T	W	T	F	**S**	**S**
		1	2	3	**4**	**5**
6	7	8	9	10	**11**	**12**
13	14	15	16	17	**18**	**19**
20	21	22	23	24	**25**	**26**
27	28	29	30	31		

August

M	T	W	T	F	**S**	**S**
					1	**2**
3	4	5	6	7	**8**	**9**
10	11	12	13	14	**15**	**16**
17	18	19	20	21	**22**	**23**
24	25	26	27	28	**29**	**30**
31						

September

M	T	W	T	F	**S**	**S**
	1	2	3	4	**5**	**6**
7	8	9	10	11	**12**	**13**
14	15	16	17	18	**19**	**20**
21	22	23	24	25	**26**	**27**
28	29	30				

October

M	T	W	T	F	**S**	**S**
			1	2	**3**	**4**
5	6	7	8	9	**10**	**11**
12	13	14	15	16	**17**	**18**
19	20	21	22	23	**24**	**25**
26	27	28	29	30	**31**	

November

M	T	W	T	F	**S**	**S**
						1
2	3	4	5	6	**7**	**8**
9	10	11	12	13	**14**	**15**
16	17	18	19	20	**21**	**22**
23	24	25	26	27	**28**	**29**
30						

December

M	T	W	T	F	**S**	**S**
	1	2	3	4	**5**	**6**
7	8	9	10	11	**12**	**13**
14	15	16	17	18	**19**	**20**
21	22	23	24	25	**26**	**27**
28	29	30	31			

31   Monday

1   Tuesday

2   Wednesday

3   Thursday

January

The North-east of England

Swallowfish, traditional kipper smokers

The Northumbrian seaside village of Seahouses is reputedly where the world's first kipper was created, in 1843, when some split herring were accidentally left overnight in a shed near a smouldering fire. Within a few years many herring sheds had been converted into smokehouses and a thriving industry was born. Over 150 years later, former trawlerman Patrick Wilkin and his wife Karen run the last working example of a traditional kipper smokehouse in Seahouses, curing their fish without dyes or additives. The herring are split, cleaned and brined, then pegged on wooden tenterhooks which keep the herring open. The smoking, which takes 12–15 hours, takes place over smouldering oak sawdust.

Ten North-eastern foods to try

Macon mutton bacon
Lindisfarne mead
Pacific oysters from the Lindisfarne oyster beds
Redesdale sheep's cheese smooth and creamy
Singin' Hinnies fried fruit scones
Stotty cakes discs of leftover dough cooked at the bottom the oven
Pan Haggerty a layered potato, onion and cheese dish
Whitley 'Goose' a cheese, onion and cream bake
Pease pudding
Alnwick stew chopped bacon forehock layered with onions and potatoes
Bacon Floddies like rostis, made from potato, onion, bacon and flour

What's good in January

Vegetables Artichoke (Jerusalem) * Brussels sprouts * Brussels tops * Cabbage (red, white and various green varieties) * Celery * Chicory * Endive * Greens (spring and winter) * Kale (and borecole) * Leek * Lettuce * Onion * Parsnip * Potato * Swede Fruit Pear, late (Concorde, Doyenne du Comice, Conference, Winter Nellis) * Rhubarb (forced) Fungi and nuts Chestnuts Fish and shellfish Cockles * Cod * Crab (brown, cock and hen) * Oyster (rock) * Whiting Game Hare * Partridge * Pheasant * Snipe * Woodcock

Kipper carbonara

Bring a large pan of water to the boil, salt it well and throw in
500g spaghetti or linguine. Meanwhile, cut the flesh off the skin of
400g kipper fillets and remove any pin bones. Slice the kipper flesh into
small strips. Fry over a low heat in a *knob of butter* for just a couple of
minutes, until cooked through. Put *4 egg yolks* and *200ml double cream*
into a large bowl. Season (going easy on the *salt*) and whisk together. As
soon as the pasta is cooked, drain it well, then return it to the still-hot
pan it was cooked in. Add the egg and cream mixture and the kipper
slices and quickly toss everything together using two forks. The finished
sauce should coat the pasta strands like silky custard. Serve straight
away, and pass the *pepper* mill around. Serves 5–6.

Leek and bacon pasty

Finely slice *4 rashers streaky bacon*. Heat *1 tbsp oil* in a frying pan and
fry the bacon until crisp. Set aside. Trim and finely slice *3 large leeks*. Add
a *knob of butter* to the bacon pan, add the leeks, season, and sweat gently
until soft and translucent. Add *1 tbsp plain flour* to the pan, mix, and cook
for a further minute. Combine with the bacon, along with *4 tbsp double
cream* and *1 tsp chopped thyme*. Roll out *600g plain shortcrust pastry* and
cut out 4 circles about 18cm in diameter. Put a pile of the leek mixture on
one half of each. Brush the edge of the pastry with *beaten egg*, and fold
over to make pasties. Crimp the edges. Put on a greased baking tray, brush
the pasties with more beaten egg and bake at 190°C/Gas Mark 5 for about
30 minutes. Eat hot or cold. Serves 4.

Marmalade and mead trifle

Put *18 dried figs*, *4 tbsp mead*, the *juice and grated zest of 1 orange*
and *¼ tsp each ground cinnamon and ground allspice* into a bowl. Mix
well and leave for at least an hour. Melt *50g dark chocolate*, then dip
18 walnut halves in it so each is half-covered. Leave on a sheet of
parchment to set. Cut *150g plain sponge cake* into small cubes and put in
the bases of 6 large wine glasses. Spoon on the figs and their liquid. Add
½ tbsp fine-cut Seville orange marmalade to each glass. Divide 500ml
chilled custard (preferably homemade) between the glasses. Lightly whip
500ml double cream and carefully swirl onto the custard. Top with the
chocolate-coated walnuts – or just a little grated chocolate, if you prefer.
Chill thoroughly before serving. Serves 6.

Friday

4

Saturday

5

Sunday

6

Notes

January

Week 1

7   Monday

- -

8   ● Tuesday

- -

9   Wednesday

- -

10   Thursday

Friday

11

Saturday

12

Bridport Farmers' Market

Sunday

13

Farmhouse breakfast week (www.hgca.com/breakfast), until Saturday 26th January

---

Notes

January

14   **Monday**

Farmhouse breakfast week continues until Saturday 26th January

15   ◗ **Tuesday**

16   **Wednesday**

17   **Thursday**

Friday **18**

Saturday **19**

Sunday **20**

Notes

January
Week 3

21   **Monday**

Farmhouse breakfast week continues until Saturday 26th January

22   ○ **Tuesday**

23   **Wednesday**

24   **Thursday**

Friday

25

Saturday

26

Sunday

27

Notes

January

28   Monday

29   Tuesday

30   ◑ Wednesday

31   Thursday

February

The East of England

Richard Haward, West Mersea oyster farmer

The Haward family has been fattening Colchester natives in the shallow creeks around Mersea Island for over 200 years. Richard and his son Joe are following in the footsteps of the Romans who started farming native oysters in Essex over 2,000 years ago. In the spring, the oysters are dredged from the deeper water of the river Blackwater, where they have been for four years or more, and brought to Richard's oyster beds in Salcott Creek. The mudflats help warm up the water and there is an abundance of food streaming in from the surrounding marsh – perfect conditions for fattening oysters. By the start of September, the bivalves are plump and ready to be picked, washed and graded. The Blackwater estuary is one of the saltiest in the country, giving these shellfish a distinctive salty flavour. Richard believes that a good oyster needs no dressing up. 'Have it in the raw,' he says, 'and bite it before you swallow so you can savour its sweet, salty tang.'

Ten Eastern foods to try

Cambridge gage the best of the old English gages, available in late summer
Stiffkey Blue (pronounced 'stookey') a grey/blue-shelled cockle
Yarmouth Bloater cold-smoked, ungutted herring, found in the autumn
Cromer crab
Careless gooseberry originally grown under Bramley apple trees, fruiting in late May and early June
D'Arcy Spice apple a late-season apple with a hot, spicy flavour
Marsh samphire a wild sea vegetable found around the coast from June to September
Norfolk Black turkey
Suffolk sweet-cure bacon
Asparagus peaks in May and June

What's good in February

Vegetables Artichoke (Jerusalem) * Brussels sprouts * Brussels tops * Cabbage (white and various green varieties) * Chicory * Endive * Greens (spring and winter) * Kale (and borecole) * Leek * Lettuce * Onion * Potato * Swede Fruit Rhubarb (forced) Fish and shellfish Cockles * Cod * Crab (brown, cock and hen) * Oyster (rock) Game Hare

Leek, celeriac and oyster broth

Heat *50g butter* and *1 tbsp olive oil* in a large pan. Add *400g celeriac*, finely diced, *100g potato*, finely diced, *2 inner stems of celery*, finely diced, the white part of *1 leek*, finely sliced, *1 small onion*, finely diced and *2 cloves garlic*, finely chopped. Cook gently for 5–10 minutes. Add *750ml fish stock* and *½ glass white wine*. Cover and cook gently for 20–25 minutes. Meanwhile, put another pan over a high heat and add ½ glass water. When it's boiling, place *6 oysters* in the pan. Cover and steam for 2 minutes until open. Remove the oyster meat and reserve the juice in the shells. Repeat with *12 more oysters*. Stir *100ml double cream* and the oyster juice into the soup. Season. Put 3 oysters in each of 6 soup plates and ladle over the hot broth. Serves 6 as a starter.

Pork chops with mustard mash

Bring a large pan of well-salted water to the boil. Peel *500g floury potatoes* and cut into equal pieces. Add to the pan of boiling water, bring back to a simmer and cook until completely tender – 12 minutes or so. Tip them into a colander and leave for at least 3 minutes to 'steam off'. Meanwhile, put *125ml full cream milk*, *60g butter*, *2 heaped tsp English mustard* and some *freshly ground black pepper* into the still-warm pan and put it over a low heat to melt the butter. Keep it hot (but not boiling), until the butter is completely melted. Rice the potatoes directly into the hot milk and butter. Stir well to get a smooth texture. Check the seasoning and keep warm while you fry *2 organic or free-range pork loin chops* in olive oil for about 5 minutes each side, or until cooked right through. Serves 2.

Bramley apple sorbet

Put *50ml water*, the *juice of ½ lemon* and *150g caster sugar* in a saucepan and bring to the boil. Peel, core and slice *1kg Bramley apples* and add to the pan. Cook at a gentle simmer, stirring regularly, until the apples are mushy. Remove from the heat, beat the mixture well, then press it through a sieve to make it really smooth. Taste and add more sugar if necessary (erring on the side of too much, as the mixture will taste less sweet when frozen). Churn the mixture in an ice cream machine. Alternatively, place in a shallow container, freeze for an hour, then beat with a fork to break up the ice crystals. Return to the freezer and repeat until you have a firm, scoop-able sorbet. Serve as a palate cleanser, or with shortbread biscuits for pudding. Serves 4–6.

Friday

1

Saturday

2

Sunday

3

Notes

February

4   **Monday**

5   **Tuesday**

Shrove Tuesday

6   **Wednesday**

Ash Wednesday

7   ● **Thursday**

Friday

8

Saturday

9

Bridport Farmers' Market

Sunday

10

Notes

February

11

National Honey Week (www.honeyassociation.com), until Sunday 17th February

12

Tuesday

13

Wednesday

14

◑ Thursday

St Valentines Day

Friday

15

Saturday

16

Sunday

17

Notes

February

18   **Monday**

19   **Tuesday**

20   **Wednesday**

21   ○ **Thursday**

Friday

22

Saturday

23

Sunday

24

Notes

February

25   **Monday**

---

26   **Tuesday**

---

27   **Wednesday**

---

28   **Thursday**

March

Northern Ireland

Pat O'Doherty, Enniskillen bacon- and ham-curer

Pat O'Doherty's pigs may well be the happiest swine around, since they spend 90 per cent of their life on their own private island. From May to June, Pat uses a traditional flat-bottomed boat called a 'cot' to ferry batches of piglets out to Inish Corkish, a low-lying island in Co. Fermanagh's Lough Earne. By July there are 250 pigs, a mix of Saddlebacks, Tamworths and Wessex, happily foraging on the island. Around November, Pat arrives with a group of local children to flush the pigs out of their dens and return them to the mainland. Pat, who runs a small butcher's shop in Enniskillen, spent over five years developing his Black Bacon. He formulated his recipe after visiting farms on both sides of the border, talking to elderly farmers and collecting ancient dry-curing techniques. His pork is cured using a traditional blend of salt, sugar and wild flower extracts, and is matured naturally for three months to create a sweet, flavourful rasher.

Ten Northern Irish foods to try

Soda bread
Strangford Loch oysters
Spiced beef or Huntsman's beef cooked, spiced, cured beef
Cruibins pickled pig's trotters
Champ creamy mashed potatoes flecked with spring onions
Boxty a cake of mashed and raw potatoes fried in a pan or on a griddle
Dulse a tangy red seaweed
Barm Brack fruited tea bread
Ulster Fry bacon, sausages, black pudding, eggs and a potato farl
Ardglass potted herrings

What's good in March

Vegetables Broccoli (purple sprouting) * Cabbage (various green varieties) * Chicory * Greens (spring and winter) * Leek * Sea kale Fruit Rhubarb (forced) Wild greens and herbs Alexanders * Chickweed * Chive * Cow parsley (aka wild chervil) * Fat hen * Nettles * Sea kale * Watercress Wild flowers and fruits Primrose (garden) Fungi, nuts and saps Birch sap Fish and shellfish Pollack * Salmon (wild) * Sea trout * Cockles * Crab (brown, cock) * Oyster (rock) Game Hare

Nettle colcannon cakes with egg and bacon

Heat *1 tbsp oil* in a pan over a medium heat, add *1 finely chopped onion* and fry until soft. Blanch *3–4 good handfuls nettle tops* in boiling water until just wilted. Drain, squeeze dry, and chop. Combine with the onion. Peel and chop *500g floury potatoes*, then boil in lightly salted water until tender. Drain and leave to steam dry. Put *50ml full cream milk* and *25g butter* in the potato pan and heat gently. Rice the potatoes into the pan and mix well. Stir in the onions and nettles. Season well. Heat *1 tbsp olive oil* in a large frying pan. Add *4 rashers bacon* and fry until crisp. Set aside and keep warm. Divide the potato mix in two and add to the pan. Press down to form flat cakes. Cook for about 5 minutes each side. When the colcannon cakes are nearly done, break *2 eggs* into the pan and fry to your liking. Put a colcannon cake and a couple of rashers of bacon on each plate, then top with a fried egg. Serves 2.

Irish stew

Trim *4 large lamb or mutton chump chops* of excess fat (but don't remove it all). Put in a large pot with *1kg floury potatoes*, peeled and halved, *2 large onions*, peeled and halved, *2 large carrots*, peeled and cut into 2–3 pieces each, *1 medium turnip*, peeled and quartered, and *2 rounded tbsp pearl barley*. Add enough water or *lamb stock* to just cover everything (about 750ml). Season well and bring to a gentle simmer. Cook, covered but with the lid slightly ajar, for 1½–2 hours, until the meat is completely tender. Check and adjust the seasoning. Serve in warm bowls or plates, with plenty of the liquor, and with *chopped parsley* sprinkled over each serving. Serves 4.

Stout fruit cake

Preheat the oven to 150°C/Gas Mark 2. Line a deep, 20cm diameter cake tin with greaseproof paper, and grease it. Beat *225g softened butter* with *225g soft, light brown sugar* until light and fluffy. Gradually beat in *2 eggs*. Combine *340g wholewheat flour*, *2 tsp baking powder*, *1 tsp mixed spice* and a pinch of *salt* in a separate bowl. Measure out *150ml stout*. Fold 2 tbsp of the flour mix into the butter and sugar, then 2 tbsp of the stout, and continue alternating until all is incorporated. Fold in *170g currants*, *170g sultanas*, *85g chopped walnuts* and the *grated zest of 1 orange*. Spoon into the tin, level the top and bake for 2¼–2½ hours, or until a skewer pressed into the middle comes out clean. Cool completely in the tin before turning out. Serves 10.

Friday ◑ 29

Saturday 1

St David's Day

Sunday 2

Mothering Sunday

Notes

March

3

4

5

6

Friday ●

7

Saturday

8

Bridport Farmers' Market

Sunday

9

Feast East Food Festival (www.tasteofanglia.com), until Monday 10th March

Notes

March

10   Monday

Feast East Food Festival (last day)
11   Tuesday

12   Wednesday

13   Thursday

Friday ◐ 14

Saturday 15

Sunday 16

Notes

March

17

St Patrick's Day

18
Tuesday

19
Wednesday

20
Thursday

Spring equinox

Friday ○

21

Good Friday

Saturday

22

Sunday

23

Easter Sunday

Notes

March

24   **Monday**

Easter Monday

25   **Tuesday**

26   **Wednesday**

27   **Thursday**

Friday

28

Exeter Festival of South West Food and Drink (www.visitsouthwest.co.uk/exeterfoodfestival),
until Sunday 30th March

Saturday ◑

29

Sunday

30

British Summertime begins

Notes

31 Monday

1 Tuesday

2 Wednesday

3 Thursday

April

The East Midlands

Ram Hall Farm, Berkswell cheese makers

In 1989, dairy farmer Stephen Fletcher decided to diversify and start milking Friesland sheep alongside his cows at Ram Hall, near Coventry. Initially he sold the milk in frozen pints, but when a local shop asked if he could make a ewe's milk cheese he rose to the challenge. Stephen knew little about the process, but he began working with a neighbouring farmer's daughter who had cheese-making experience. Using a recipe for Caerphilly as their initial inspiration, they were soon able to develop the award-winning Berkswell, a firm but creamy cheese with a sweet, nutty flavour. The cheese rapidly gained fans all over the country, and Stephen was able to expand and add two soft, mould-ripened sheep's cheeses to the dairy's repertoire: Marlow and Kelsey Lane. His flock has expanded to over a thousand sheep, but despite high demand, Berkswell is still made by hand, daily, by chief cheese-maker Linda Dutch.

(Technically, Berkswell is just inside the West rather than the East Midlands, but this is such a lovely cheese we felt justified in stretching our borders slightly.)

Ten foods to try from the East Midlands

Stilton cheese
Lincolnshire sausages
Melton Mowbray pork pie a raised pie filled with uncured pork
Haslet brined pork and offal cooked in long loaves
Bakewell pudding a puff pastry tart with strawberry or raspberry jam and an almond and egg custard topping
Lincolnshire plum bread a rich, spiced fruit bread
Lincoln Red cattle
Lincolnshire stuffed chine a bacon pig's backbone with a parsley stuffing
Good King Henry a herb also known as Lincolnshire spinach or wild spinach
Sage Derby cheese

What's good in April

Vegetable Broccoli (purple sprouting) * Cabbage (various green varieties) * Cauliflower * Greens (spring and winter) * Lettuce * Radish * Sea kale * Sorrel * Watercress Fruit Rhubarb (forced) * Rhubarb (outdoor) Wild greens and herbs Alexanders * Chickweed * Dandelion * Fat hen * Hogweed shoots * Hop shoots * Meadowsweet (leaves) * Nettles * Sea kale * Sea spinach * Sorrel * Chive * Cow parsley (aka wild chervil) * Watercress * Wild garlic * Wild rocket leaves Wild flowers and fruits Primrose (garden) Fungi and nuts Morel * St George's mushroom Fish and shellfish Cockles * Crab (brown, cock) * Pollack * Salmon (wild) * Sea trout Game Wood pigeon

Sea beet and Berkswell tart

Prepare and blind-bake a *25cm shortcrust pastry shell*. Set the oven to 180°C/Gas Mark 4. Heat a *knob of butter* in a frying pan over a medium heat and add *2 large onions*, finely sliced. Fry gently, until soft. Drop *200g sea beet leaves* (or use 400g spinach) into a pan of boiling water and cook for a couple of minutes until wilted. Drain, squeeze dry and coarsely chop. Mix with the onions. Season well. Arrange the sea beet and onion mixture over the pastry case. Scatter on *150g grated Berkswell cheese*. Beat together *250ml milk*, *250ml double cream*, *3 eggs* and *2 egg yolks*, season and pour into the tart. Bake for about 40 minutes or until lightly set and golden brown. Serve warm or cold. Serves 6.

Faggots

Preheat the oven to 180°C/Gas Mark 4. Roughly chop, then coarsely mince *250g fresh pig's liver*, *250g fresh fatty pork scraps or coarse sausage meat*, *1 fresh pig's heart* and *100g ham or bacon scraps*. Combine with *100g fresh breadcrumbs or oatmeal*, plus a few finely chopped *sage and thyme leaves* and a good pinch each of *ground mace* and *allspice*. Mix together thoroughly. Shape into 6 balls. Wrap each in a square of *caul fat or 2 stretched rashers of streaky bacon*. Flatten the balls slightly and place in a baking tin or ovenproof dish in which they fit fairly snugly. Bake for 50–60 minutes, basting once or twice. They will be slightly shrunken and nicely brown when done. Serve at once with onion gravy, or leave to go cold and serve with mustard. Serves 6.

Grantham gingerbread

Preheat the oven to 170°C/Gas Mark 3 and grease a large baking sheet. Beat together *200g caster sugar* and *100g soft butter* until light and fluffy. Beat in *1 egg*. Combine *200g plain flour* with *½ tsp baking powder*, *1–2 tsp ground ginger* and a pinch of *salt*. Fold into the dough. Take heaped dessertspoonfuls of the mixture and shape into balls. Place these on the baking sheet and squash slightly. Bake for about 15 minutes until light golden, then cool on a rack. Makes about 20.

Friday 4

Saturday 5

Sunday ● 6

Notes

April

7 Monday

8 Tuesday

9 Wednesday

10 Thursday

Friday **11**

Saturday ◐ **12**

Bridport Farmers' Market

Sunday **13**

Notes

April

14 Monday

15 Tuesday

16 Wednesday

17 Thursday

Friday

18

Saturday

19

Sunday ○

20

Notes

21   Monday

22   Tuesday

23   Wednesday

St George's Day

24   Thursday

Friday **25**

Saturday **26**

Sunday **27**

Notes

April

28 ◑ **Monday**

29 **Tuesday**

30 **Wednesday**

1 **Thursday**

May

London

Growing Communities, London organic box scheme and farmers' market

Growing Communities set up London's first organic box scheme in 1994. Originally there were just 30 customers; now the group packs over 600 bags of fresh, organic local produce every week, which customers collect from three pick-up points around Hackney. Some of the produce is supplied by the organisation's three small organic market gardens run by volunteers in Hackney. These are possibly the smallest sites in Britain to have won the Soil Association stamp, and certainly the first certified organic food-growing plots in London. Growing Communities specialise in salads, and they pride themselves on creating the best mixed bags, containing a huge range of leaves, herbs and flowers. When in season, they also offer asparagus cut from their beds in Clissold Park. In 2003 the group set up the Stoke Newington Farmers' Market, the first and only all-organic weekly farmers' market in the UK. This is now a major outlet for local producers and over 435 acres of land has been converted to organic farming by the farmers who attend the market. Growing Communities believe they have found a practical and positive way to put inner city dwellers in touch with their local food network.

Ten London foods to try

Wild mushrooms from Epping Forest, Hampstead Heath and Wimbledon Common (the season peaks between late summer and late autumn)
London-cure smoked salmon lighter than traditional Scottish cures
London honey
Lox and bagels
Gentlemen's Relish or Patum Peperium spiced anchovy relish
Richmond Maids of Honour sweet tartlets
Jellied Eels
London gin
Eel pie and mash
London Particular split pea and ham soup

What's good in May

Vegetable Asparagus * Cabbage (various green varieties) * Carrot * Cauliflower * Lettuce * Radish * Rocket * Sea kale * Sorrel * Watercress
Fruit Rhubarb (outdoor) Wild greens and herbs Broom buds * Chive * Dandelions * Fat hen * Hogweed shoots * Hop shoots * Meadowsweet (leaves) * Sea spinach * Sorrel * Watercress * Wild fennel * Wild garlic * Wild rocket (leaves) Fungi and nuts Morel * Pignut * St George's mushroom
Fish and shellfish Crab (spider) * Crayfish, signal (freshwater) * Cuttlefish * Pollack * Salmon (wild) * Sea trout Game Wood pigeon

Spring crudités with caper and anchovy mayo

To make the mayo, combine *100ml olive oil* and *200ml groundnut oil*. Whisk *2 egg yolks* together, then start adding the mixed oil a few drops at a time. Once the mayonnaise has 'taken', increase the flow to a steady trickle. It should be very thick by the time you've finished adding the oil. Mash *¼ garlic clove* and finely chop a *50g tin anchovies*, and a *generous tbsp capers*. Stir all into the mayonnaise, followed by a *squeeze of lemon* and a few twists of *black pepper*. Taste and adjust the seasoning. Leave to stand for half an hour, then give it another quick whisk before serving with a selection of crudités such as *baby carrots*, very fresh *asparagus*, tiny young *lettuce hearts* and crisp *radishes*. Serves 4–6.

Elderflower panna cotta

Combine *100ml whole milk*, *400ml double cream* and *40g caster sugar* in a pan. Tie up *3–4 large heads elderflower* in a piece of muslin and add to the pan. Bring just to the boil (but don't let it bubble), then set aside for half an hour or so. Remove the elderflower. Soak *3 leaves gelatine* in cold water for 5–10 minutes until soft. Lift out the sheets, shake off as much water as you can, then add to the warm cream. Stir until dissolved. Allow to cool to room temperature, stirring from time to time. Pour the cooled mixture into 4 125ml moulds or ramekins and chill until set (at least 4 hours). To turn out, dip the moulds very briefly in hot water then turn upside down and give them a shake. Serve each panna cotta with a spoonful or two of lightly cooked, sweetened gooseberries. Serves 4.

Chelsea buns

Combine *150ml milk* with *225g melted butter*. Stir in *5g dried yeast*. In a separate bowl, combine *550g strong white bread flour*, *50g caster sugar* and *10g salt*, then add the yeasty liquid and *1 beaten egg*. Mix to a dough, then knead for 10 minutes until smooth. Cover and leave to rise for an hour, until doubled in size. Meanwhile brush a 30cm square, deep baking tray with melted butter and dust with caster sugar. Tip out the dough, dust with flour and roll out to a rectangle 60cm by 40cm. Brush with *25g melted butter*, leaving a 2cm strip across the top. Sprinkle *100g caster sugar* and *200g currants* over the dough. Roll to make a long sausage. Wet the unbuttered strip at the top and seal the roll. Cut into 9 equal pieces, turning each on its end. Place these in 3 rows of 3 in the baking tray. Leave until they have doubled in size again. Preheat the oven to 200°C/Gas Mark 6. Bake for about 20 minutes. Heat together *50ml milk* and *50g caster sugar*, and brush this over the hot buns. Leave to cool. Serves 9.

Friday 2

Saturday 3

Sunday 4

Whitsunday
Compost Awareness Week (www.compostawarenessweek.org.uk), until Saturday 10th May

---

Notes

May

5   ● **Monday**

Early May Bank Holiday
Compost Awareness Week continues until Saturday 10th May

---

6   **Tuesday**

---

7   **Wednesday**

---

8   **Thursday**

Royal Windsor Food and Drink Festival (www.royal-windsor-horse-show.co.uk), until Sunday 11th May

Friday

9

Henley Food Festival (www.henleyfoodfestival.co.uk), until Saturday 10th May
Christchurch Food Festival (www.christchurchfoodfest.co.uk), until Friday 16th May

Saturday

10

Bridport Farmers' Market

Sunday

11

Notes

May

12

Christchurch Food Festival continues until Friday 16th May

13

Tuesday

14

Wednesday

Balmoral Show (www.balmoralshow.co.uk), until Friday 16th May

15

Thursday

Devon County Show (www.devoncountyshow.co.uk), until Saturday 17th May

rivercottage.net

Friday

16

Saturday

17

Derbyshire Food Festival (www.derbyshirefoodfestival.co.uk), until Monday 26th May
Royal Welsh Smallholder and Garden Festival (www.rwas.co.uk), until Sunday 18th May

Sunday

18

Notes

May

19   **Monday**

National Vegetarian Week (www.vegsoc.org), until Sunday 25th May
British Tomato Week (www.britishtomatoes.co.uk), until Sunday 25th May
Derbyshire Food Festival continues until Monday 26th May

20   ○ **Tuesday**

21   **Wednesday**

22   **Thursday**

Friday **23**

Saturday **24**

English Wine Week (www.englishwineweek.co.uk), until Sunday 1st June
Hertfordshire County Show (www.hertsshow.com), until Sunday 25th May

Sunday **25**

Notes

26

Spring Bank Holiday
Surrey County Show (www.surreycountyshow.co.uk)
Derbyshire Food Festival (last day)
English Wine Week continues until Sunday 1st June

27
Tuesday

28
◑ **Wednesday**

Suffolk Show (www.suffolkshow.co.uk), until Thursday 29th May
Royal Bath and West Show (www.bathandwest.com), until Saturday 31st May

29
Thursday

June

Wales and the Isle of Man

Graig Farm Organics

Wales has long been famous for its mountain lamb, but finding meat from a pure-bred animal that has lived on hilltop vegetation is becoming increasingly difficult. Many of the small, hardy breeds which are suited to rocky upland terrain are crossbred with lowland breeds, with the progeny fattened up on lusher pasture lower down. They sometimes even have their diet supplemented with cereal pellets. However, Bob and Carolyn Kennard of Graig Farm Organics in Powys source their mountain lambs from traditional mountain breeds, including Welsh Mountain, Welsh Speckleface, Badger Face and Beulah, on upland farms. They live, breed and lamb naturally with very little intervention from the shepherd, and graze mostly on mountain pasture, heather, wild herbs and flowers, with little or no supplementary feeding. This, coupled with their active lifestyles, gives their meat a fantastic flavour and texture. They are slow-growing and smaller than many other breeds: a whole leg feeds two or three people. They lamb from March to May and the meat is sold, as lamb, from July until Christmas. After this, it becomes known as hogget (lamb in its second year). Meat from sheep that have reached two years of age is called Welsh mountain mutton.

Ten Welsh foods to try

Sewin or seatrout available from foxglove time until the autumn
Laverbread seaweed cooked into a thick purée
Welsh black beef
Cawl a rich stew of leeks, bacon and lamb
Bara Brith fruited tea bread
Black Mountain honey
Goat's cheeses
Caerphilly cheese
Penclawdd cockles
Manx kippers

What's good in June

Vegetable Asparagus * Broad bean * Carrot * Cauliflower * Lettuce * Pea (including sugar snap) * Purslane * Radish * Rocket * Sorrel * Watercress Fruit Cherry (European) * Gooseberries * Rhubarb (outdoor) * Strawberries Wild greens and herbs * Broom buds * Horseradish * Sea spinach * Wild fennel Wild flowers and fruits Elderflower Fungi and nuts St George's mushroom * Pignut Fish and shellfish Black beam * Crab (spider) * Crayfish, signal (freshwater) * Cuttlefish * Mackerel * Pollack * Salmon (wild) * Sea bass * Trout, river (brown and rainbow) * Trout, sea Game Wood pigeon

Slow-braised shoulder of hogget with Moroccan spices

Preheat the oven to 220°C/Gas Mark 7. In a dry frying pan, toast *1 tsp each cumin seeds, coriander seeds, fennel seeds and black peppercorns*, along with a *3cm piece cinnamon*, until fragrant. Crush to a powder in a pestle and mortar, then combine with a pinch *cayenne pepper or chilli powder*, *2 tsp sweet paprika, 1 clove garlic*, finely chopped, the finely chopped leaves of *2 large sprigs rosemary, 2 tsp salt* and *1 tbsp olive oil*. Rub half the mixture all over a *whole shoulder of hogget (or lamb)*. Roast for 30 minutes. Remove from the oven and use the back of a wooden spoon to rub the remaining spice mix over the joint. Pour a glass of water into the tin (not over the meat), cover with foil, return to the oven, reduce the heat to 120°C/Gas Mark ½ and cook for 6 hours or until the meat is falling off the bone. Serve with griddled fennel. Serves 6–10.

Spaghetti with sea trout and samphire

Pick over *500g marsh samphire*, removing the entire root and any tough stems. Wash it thoroughly. Break up any larger pieces. Bring a large pan of water to the boil, *salt* it generously and drop in *350g spaghetti*. Boil for 8–9 minutes, or until al dente. Add the samphire to the pan for the last two minutes of cooking time. Meanwhile, heat a little *olive oil* in a frying pan over a medium heat. Season *500g wild sea trout fillet*, add to the pan and fry for 2–3 minutes each side. Flake the trout off its skin, removing any bones that you find. Drain the spaghetti and samphire and return to the hot pan. Add a *good knob of butter*, a dash of *olive oil* and plenty of *black pepper* and toss together. Transfer to warm plates and scatter over the flaked trout. Finish off with a *squeeze of lemon juice* and a few more twists of black pepper. Serves 4.

Rhubarb creams

Put *1kg trimmed, chopped rhubarb*, the *juice of 1 orange* and *125g caster sugar* in a pan. Bring to a gentle simmer, then cook for about 5 minutes, until soft. Use a sieve to strain off a little of the juice (which is delicious mixed with sparkling white wine). Divide the compote between 6–8 ramekins. Chill thoroughly. Whip *330ml double cream* until very thick, then spread carefully over the chilled rhubarb. Return to the fridge until the cream is thoroughly cold. Preheat your grill to its highest heat. Sprinkle a thin, even layer of *soft brown sugar* over the chilled ramekins – use no more than a dessertspoon per ramekin. Place the ramekins under the hot grill until the sugar begins to melt and bubble. Return to the fridge until they are quite cold, then serve. Serves 6–8.

Friday

30

- -

Saturday

31

- -

Sunday

1

- -

Notes

June

2   Monday

3   ● Tuesday

4   Wednesday

5   Thursday

Royal Cornwall Show (www.royalcornwallshow.org), until Saturday 7th June
South of England Show (www.seas.org.uk/shwidx.asp), until Saturday 7th June

Friday

6

Saturday

7

Bridport Farmers' Market

Sunday

8

Notes

June

9 Monday

10 ◐ Tuesday

11 Wednesday

12 Thursday

Friday

13

East of England Show (www.eastofengland.org.uk), until Sunday 15th June

Saturday

14

Sunday

15

Father's Day

Notes

June

16
Monday

17
Tuesday

Cheshire County Show (www.cheshirecountyshow.org.uk), until Wednesday 18th June

18
○ **Wednesday**

19
Thursday

Royal Highland Show (www.royalhighlandshow.org), until Sunday 22nd June

Friday

20

Summer Solstice
Glastonbury Festival (www.glastonburyfestival.co.uk), until Sunday 22nd June

Saturday

21

World Stinging Nettle Eating Championships and Beer Festival (www.thebottleinn.co.uk),
until Sunday 22nd June
Hampshire Food Festival (www.hampshirefare.co.uk), until Sunday 6th July
Pembrokeshire Fish Week (www.pembrokeshire.gov.uk/foodanddrink), until Sunday 29th June

Sunday

22

Notes

June

23   **Monday**

Hampshire Food Festival continues until Sunday 6th July
Pembrokeshire Fish Week continues until Sunday 29th June

24   **Tuesday**

25   **Wednesday**

26   ◑ **Thursday**

Friday

27

Saturday

28

Colchester Food and Drink Festival (www.colchesterfoodanddrinkfestival.co.uk),
until Sunday 29th June

Sunday

29

The Royal Show (www.royalshow.org.uk), until Wednesday 2nd July

Notes

June

30   **Monday**

Hampshire Food Festival continues until Sunday 6th July
The Royal Show continues until Wednesday 2nd July

1   **Tuesday**

2   **Wednesday**

3   ● **Thursday**

July

The South-east of England

The Park Farm Community Cherry Orchard Project

In the 1950s, English cherry orchards covered over 18,000 acres of the country. Today they cover a little over 950 acres. One reason for this decline is that traditional 'standard' cherry trees grow up to 60 feet high, and harvesting them requires skilled labour. By the 1980s a lack of pickers and the development of new dwarf varieties meant that our magnificent standard cherry orchards were in danger of disappearing. Kent farmer Pip Neaves worked with his parish councils at Lynstead and Kingsdown to encourage interest in local cherry farming. Pip still harvests the cherries from his 150 standard trees in the traditional way, using a special 50-foot cherry ladder. Boosted by a Heritage Initiative grant, the Park Farm Community Cherry Orchard Project enabled Pip's orchard to be used for events such as Cherry Day (20th July this year) and maypole-dancing on Blossom Day. The project has started a wave of support to save other local orchards, including those growing the sour Morello cherries used to make traditional cherry brandy.

Ten South-eastern foods to try

Blenheim orange a late-season apple suitable for eating and cooking
Leveller gooseberry a sweet dessert gooseberry ready in late July
Kentish cobnuts in season mid-August to October
Hampshire watercress available throughout the summer
Signal crayfish
Aylesbury duck
Southdown sheep
Hop shoots eat like green beans in April and May
Whitstable oyster
English sparkling wine from the vineyards of Sussex and Kent

What's good in July

Vegetable Artichoke (globe) * Beetroot * Broad bean * Carrot * Cauliflower * Courgette * French beans (whole pod) * Garlic * Kohlrabi * Lamb's lettuce * Onion * Pak choi * Pea (including sugar snap) * Potato * Purslane * Radish * Rocket * Samphire * Sorrel * Spinach * Tomato * Watercress Fruit * Apricot * Blackcurrants * Blueberries * Cherry (European) * Cherry (UK) * Gooseberries * Raspberries * Redcurrants * Rhubarb (outdoor) * Strawberries * White currants * Worcesterberries Wild greens and herbs * Marsh samphire * Horseradish * Wild fennel Wild flowers and fruits * Elderflower * Wild strawberries Fungi and nuts Chanterelle * Chicken of the Wood * Summer Truffle * Pignut Fish and shellfish * Black beam * Crab (brown, hen and spider) * Crayfish, signal (freshwater) * Cuttlefish * Lobster * Mackerel * Pollack * Scallop * Sea bass * Trout, river (brown and rainbow) * Trout, sea Game Rabbit * Wood pigeon

Cherry batter pudding

Preheat the oven to 180°C/Gas Mark 4. Butter a 25–28cm diameter round ceramic dish. Toss *450g stoned cherries* with *25g caster sugar* and spread in the dish. Sift *125g plain flour* and a pinch of *salt* into a bowl and stir in *another 50g caster sugar*. Make a well in the middle and stir in *3 lightly beaten eggs*. Mix well, drawing in the flour from the sides, then beat in *300ml milk* to create a smooth batter. Pour over the cherries and bake for 35 minutes. Eat lukewarm, dusted with icing sugar, with cream. Serves 8.

Watercress soup

Melt *50g butter* in a large pan over a low heat, then add *1 finely chopped onion*. Sweat until the onion is soft but not brown. Add *1 litre vegetable or chicken stock* and bring to the boil, then add *4 good fistfuls well trimmed watercress*. Bring back to the boil and simmer for just a minute. Place in a blender with *2 rice cakes* and process until smooth. Return the soup to the pan, reheat thoroughly without boiling, and season to taste with *nutmeg*, *salt* and *pepper*. Serve in warmed bowls. To make the dish more substantial, add a poached egg to each bowl. Serves 4.

Blanc de blancs jellies

Put *12 gelatine leaves* to soak in a little water for 5 minutes (or follow the packet instructions for setting 1 litre of liquid). Put *125g caster sugar*, *175ml dry sherry*, *250ml water*, the *grated zest and juice of 1 orange and 1 lemon* and *500ml sparkling white wine* (such as Sussex blanc de blancs or champagne) in a large pan. Stir over a low heat until the sugar has dissolved. Add the soaked gelatine leaves and stir to dissolve them too. Remove from the heat and leave to cool a little. Pour the jelly into 6 serving glasses – or into 6 moulds if you want to turn the jelly out. Once cooled to room temperature, transfer to the fridge to set. Serve with fresh raspberries. Serves 6.

Friday   4

Saturday   5

Sunday   6

Notes

---

7   **Monday**

8   **Tuesday**

Great Yorkshire Show (www.greatyorkshireshow.org.uk), until Thursday 10th July

9   **Wednesday**

10   **◐ Thursday**

Friday

11

Kent Show (www.kentshowground.co.uk) until Sunday 13th July

Saturday

12

Bridport Farmers' Market

Sunday

13

Notes

July

14   **Monday**

15   **Tuesday**

16   **Wednesday**

17   **Thursday**

Friday ○

18

Saturday

19

Whitstable Oyster Festival (www.whitstableoysterfestival.co.uk), until Sunday 20th July
Cumberland Show (www.cumberlandshow.co.uk)

Sunday

20

Notes

21   **Monday**

Royal Welsh Show (www.rwas.co.uk), until Thursday 24th July

22   **Tuesday**

23   **Wednesday**

24   **Thursday**

Friday ☽   **25**

Royal Norfolk Show (www.royalnorfolkshow.co.uk), until Saturday 26th June

Saturday   **26**

Border Union Show (www.buas.org), until Sunday 27th July
CLA Game Fair (www.gamefair.co.uk), until Sunday 27th July
Tavistock Food and Drink Festival (www.tavistockfoodfestival.co.uk), until Sunday 27th July

Sunday   **27**

Notes

July

28   **Monday**

29   **Tuesday**

New Forest and Hampshire Show (www.newforestshow.co.uk), until Thursday 31st July
Nantwich International Cheese Show (www.nantwichshow.co.uk), until Wednesday 30th July

30   **Wednesday**

31   **Thursday**

August

Scotland

John Mellis, bee keeper

Scottish bee keeper John Mellis works hard to achieve distinctive flavours in his honey, driving his hives around the countryside to find the best flower sources for his bees. The bees start work early in May, taking nectar from hawthorn and sycamore flowers to produce a dark, nutty honey. They then make blossom honey from willow and clover, as well as the very distinctive lime blossom honey. From July onwards, John moves 250 hives onto the heather-blanketed hillsides of Dumfries and Galloway. Here they feed initially on bell heather, which creates a port-coloured honey, but it is the later flowering ling heather that gives the most highly prized product of all: John's very best heather honey.

Ten Scottish foods to try

Finnan haddies cold-smoked, whole haddock
Arbroth smokies hot-smoked, gutted haddock
Blaeberries a wild relation of the blueberry, appearing in late summer
Tayberries a cross between a raspberry and blackberry; look for them in July and August
Atholl brose a pudding made from oat milk, sweetened with honey
Spoots razor clams
Neeps and tatties mashed swede or turnip with potato
Cullen skink smoked haddock and potato soup
Stovies bubble and squeak
Lanark Blue cheese blue-veined ewe's milk cheese

What's good in August

Vegetables Artichoke (globe) * Aubergine * Beetroot * Broad beans * Broccoli (Calabrese) * Cabbage (various green varieties) * Carrot * Cauliflower * Chard * Courgette * Cucumber * Fennel * French bean (whole pod) * Garlic * Kohlrabi * Lamb's lettuce * Lettuce * Onions * Pak choi * Pea (including sugar snap) * Potato * Purslane * Radish * Rocket * Runner bean * Salsify (and scorzonera) * Samphire * Sorrel * Spinach * Sweetcorn * Tomato * Watercress **Fruits** Apple, early (Discovery, George Cave, Redsleeves) * Apricot * Blackberries (cultivated) * Blackcurrants * Blueberries * Loganberries * Plum * Raspberries * Redcurrants * White currants * Worcesterberries **Wild greens and herbs** Horseradish * Marsh samphire * Wild fennel **Wild flowers and fruits** * Bilberries (aka blaeberries) * Blackberries * Bullace * Wild strawberries **Fungi and nuts** Cep (aka Porcini) * Chanterelle * Chicken of the Wood * Field mushroom * Giant Puffball * Hazelnut * Horse mushroom * Oyster mushroom * Parasol * Summer Truffle **Fish and shellfish** * Black beam * Crab (brown, hen and spider) * Crayfish, signal (freshwater) * Lobster * Mackerel * Pollack * Prawn * Scallop * Sea bass * Squid * Trout, river (brown and rainbow) **Game** Rabbit * Wood pigeon

Raspberry honey cranachan

Spread *50g rolled oats or medium oatmeal* on a sheet of foil on a grill pan. Toast until golden. Combine a *284ml carton double cream* and *2 tbsp whisky* and whip until the cream holds soft peaks. Loosely fold in *2 tbsp heather honey*, the toasted oats and *250g raspberries*. Spoon into glasses and serve. Serves 4.

Roast grouse with berries and thyme

Clip off the wings of *2 grouse*. Brown in a little oil in a frying pan, along with the birds' *giblets* (not the livers), *1 chopped carrot* and *1 chopped onion*. Transfer to a small pan, with a *bay leaf*, a good splash of *red wine* and enough water to cover everything. Simmer for an hour, strain, then boil to reduce by half. Preheat the oven to 230°C/Gas Mark 8. Smear a little *butter* over the grouse, season, then cover each breast with *2 rashers streaky bacon*. Inside each bird, put a few *raspberries, blackberries or tayberries* and a *generous sprig thyme*. Roast for 10 minutes, remove the bacon and quickly baste the birds. Cook them for a further 10–15 minutes, depending on their size and whether or not you like the meat a little pink. Scrape the berries and thyme from the birds back into the tin, then set the birds aside to rest. To make the gravy, skim off any fat from the roasting tin. Heat on the hob at a medium heat and sprinkle in *1 tsp flour*. Stir into a paste with the juices, scraping up any caramelised bits. Add some of the stock to help the process. Strain these juices into a clean pan, add the remaining stock, and simmer until the intensity of flavour is just right (add a little *redcurrant or raspberry jelly* if it needs sweetness). Season. Serve each bird with the bacon, some steamed greens and the gravy. Serves 2.

Langoustines with garlic butter

Put *16 live langoustines* in the freezer for 40–50 minutes to sedate them. Meanwhile, crush *2 cloves garlic* with a little *salt* to make a paste. Gently melt *100g unsalted butter* in a small pan. Add the crushed garlic, a *squeeze of lemon juice* and *1 tbsp chopped parsley* and stir briefly over a low heat to very lightly cook the garlic. Season, then set aside while you cook the langoustines. Bring a large pan of heavily salted water to the boil (30g salt per litre of water). Add the sedated langoustines and, once the water returns to the boil, cook for 4–6 minutes, depending on their size. Drain and leave to cool a little, then serve warm, for people to shell themselves and dip in the warm garlic butter. Serves 4.

Friday ●

1

Saturday

2

Sunday

3

Notes

4 Monday

5 Tuesday

6 Wednesday

7 Thursday

Friday ☉

8

Saturday

9

Bridport Farmers' Market

Sunday

10

Notes

---

11   **Monday**

12   **Tuesday**

13   **Wednesday**

14   **Thursday**

Friday **15**

Saturday ○ **16**

Isle of Wight Garlic Festival (www.thegarlicfarm.co.uk), until Sunday 17th August

Sunday **17**

Notes

18

19

20

21

Melplash Show (www.melplashshow.co.uk)

Friday 22

Saturday ◑ 23

Sunday 24

Notes

August

25

Summer Bank Holiday

26

27

28

Bucks County Show (www.buckscountyshow.co.uk)

Friday

29

Saturday ●

30

Sunday

31

Notes

1   **Monday**

Brighton and Hove Food and Drink Festival (www.brightonfoodfestival.co.uk), until Tuesday 30th September

2 **Tuesday**

3 **Wednesday**

4 **Thursday**

September

The North-west of England

Cumbria Wild Game

Gamekeeper Steve Pymm organises shooting parties and deer stalking at Greystoke Castle, near Penrith. In order to ensure that the game from his shoots is properly inspected, transported, stored and prepared to the highest standard, Steve set up Cumbria Wild Game, which enabled him to handle the game himself, from estate to plate, and give his customers a full account of its provenance. Cumbria is blessed with a rich game larder and Steve has access to a wide variety of birds and beasts, but his favourite quarry are the wild, native roe deer, which live in small family groups around Greystoke. Steve believes that the distinctive flavour and fine texture of the venison from these deer reflects their varied natural diet of young tree shoots, clean pasture, wild flowers and herbs.

Ten North-western foods to try

Black pudding
Herdwick sheep a hardy Lake District breed
Morecambe Bay potted shrimps
Arctic char trout-like fish from Lake Windermere
Chester pie a precursor of the lemon meringue
Eccles cake puff pastry with a currant filling
Liverpool Lobscouse a lamb and vegetable stew with dried peas
Black peas or carlings cooked small brown pigeon peas
Damsons dripping from the trees in August and September
Lancashire cheese the ultimate toasting cheese

What's good in September

Vegetables Artichoke (globe) * Aubergine * Beetroot * Borlotti bean (for podding) * Broccoli (Calabrese) * Cabbage (various green varieties) * Carrot * Cauliflower * Chard * Courgette * Cucumber * Fennel * Garlic * Kale (and borecole) * Kohlrabi * Lamb's lettuce * Onion * Pak choi * Peppers and chillies * Pumpkin (and squash) * Rocket * Runner bean * Salsify (and scorzonera) * Sorrel * Spinach * Sweetcorn * Tomato * Watercress Fruit Apple, early (Discovery, George Cave, Redsleeves) * Apple, late (Egremont Russet, Blenheim Orange, Orleans Reinette) * Blackberries * Blueberries * Damson * Greengage * Loganberries * Pear, early-mid (Beth, Williams, Merton Pride) * Plum Wild greens and herbs Horseradish Wild flowers and fruits Bilberries (aka blaeberries) * Blackberries * Bullace * Elderberries * Juniper berries Fungi and Nuts Cep (aka Porcini) * Chanterelle * Chicken of the Wood * Field mushroom * Giant Puffball * Hazelnut * Horse mushroom * Oyster mushroom (pleurottes) * Parasol * Shaggy Ink Cap * Summer Truffle Fish and shellfish Black beam * Crab (brown, hen and spider) * Crayfish, signal (freshwater) * Eel * Lobster * Mackerel * Mussel * Oyster * Prawns * Scallop * Sea bass * Sprat * Squid * Trout, river (brown and rainbow) * Wild salmon Game Goose (farmed) * Grey squirrel * Grouse * Mallard * Rabbit * Wood pigeon

Venison loin with wild mushrooms

Preheat the oven to 200°C/Gas Mark 6. In a spice mill, grind *10 peppercorns, 2 bay leaves, 4 juniper berries* and *2 pinches flaky sea salt* to a fine powder. Scatter this over a *500g piece trimmed venison loin*. Rub in lightly. Heat an ovenproof frying pan over a high heat, and add *1 tbsp olive oil*. Add the venison and sear it, turning it so each surface is well-browned. Transfer the pan to the oven and cook for 10 minutes. Remove the meat from the pan and set aside to rest for 20 minutes. Put the pan back over a medium heat. Throw in *100g diced unsmoked bacon* and cook until crisp. Add *a few handfuls cleaned, trimmed wild mushrooms*, toss with the bacon, and cook until tender. Add *25g butter* to the pan and stir it in to the mushrooms. Season to taste and sprinkle over *1 tbsp chopped parsley*. Spoon the mushrooms and bacon onto 4 warmed plates. Slice the venison and arrange alongside. Serve with a mixed green salad. Serves 4.

Kale with potted shrimp butter

Steam or boil *700g trimmed curly kale* for 3–4 minutes, so it still has a bit of crunch. Drain, return to the warm pan, cover and keep warm. Take a *pot (around 60g) Morecambe Bay potted shrimps* and roughly chop them. Heat them in a small pan with the *seasoned butter* from the pot. Add *a little extra butter* (say, 50g) and a good pinch of *cayenne pepper*. Cook very gently for a couple of minutes to marry the flavours. Arrange the kale on warmed plates and spoon the shrimp butter over and around it. Serves 4 as a starter.

Westmorland damson crumble

Preheat the oven to 190°C/Gas Mark 5. Put *750g washed, destalked damsons* into a 1.5 litre pie dish. Sprinkle with *100g caster sugar*. Rub *125g cold, cubed butter* into *200g plain flour* until the mixture resembles coarse breadcrumbs. Stir in *75g Demerara sugar*. Scatter this mixture evenly over the damsons. Bake for 30–40 minutes or until the topping is golden and the damsons soft and bubbling. Serve hot with lots of cold cream or warm custard. Watch out for the stones. Serves 6.

Friday

5

Ludlow Food Festival (www.foodfestival.co.uk), until Sunday 7th September

Saturday

6

Dorset Show (www.dorsetcountyshow.co.uk), until Sunday 7th September
Soil Association Organic Fortnight (www.soilassociation.org), until Sunday 21st September
Soil Association Organic Food Festival (www.soilassociation.org), until Sunday 7th September
Sturminster Cheese Festival (www.cheesefestival.co.uk), until Sunday 7th September

Sunday ◑

7

Notes

September

8   **Monday**

Brighton and Hove Food and Drink Festival continues until Tuesday 30th September
Soil Association Organic Fortnight continues until Sunday 21st September

9   **Tuesday**

10   **Wednesday**

11   **Thursday**

Friday

12

Saturday

13

Abergavenny Food Festival (www.abergavennyfoodfestival.com) until Sunday 14th September
Bridport Farmers' Market

Sunday

14

Notes

September

15 ○ **Monday**

Brighton and Hove Food and Drink Festival continues until Tuesday 30th September
Soil Association Organic Fortnight continues until Sunday 21st September

16 **Tuesday**

17 **Wednesday**

18 **Thursday**

Friday

19

York Festival of Food and Drink (www.yorkfestivaloffoodanddrink.com), until Sunday 28th September

Saturday

20

British Food Fortnight (www.britishfoodfortnight.co.uk), until Sunday 5th October

Sunday

21

Notes

September

22

Autumn Equinox
Brighton and Hove Food and Drink Festival continues until Tuesday 30th September
York Festival of Food and Drink continues until Sunday 28th September
British Food Fortnight continues until Sunday 5th October

23
Tuesday

24
Wednesday

25
Thursday

Friday 26

Saturday 27

The Great British Cheese Festival (www.thecheeseweb.com), until Sunday 28th September

Sunday 28

Notes

September

29

Brighton and Hove Food and Drink Festival continues until Tuesday 30th September
British Food Fortnight continues until Sunday 5th October

30

Tuesday

1

Wednesday

2

Thursday

October

The South-west of England

Orchard Link, saving traditional apple orchards

Orchard Link was established by a group of campaigners, local authority advisors, cider-makers and orchard owners to help save Devon's apple heritage. As well as offering advice on restoring old orchards Orchard Link also plant new ones, often grafting rare local varieties onto new rootstock. In the autumn, they take their apple presses to community pressing events or hire them to local groups to process their own harvests. They even have cider-making workshops. Orchard Link can sell your surplus apples on their farmers' market stalls, or put you in touch with local cider-makers who want to buy your fruit. With just five commercial apple farms remaining in the whole of the South-west, and roughly two out of three apples sold in supermarkets coming from abroad, projects like this are crucial in keeping our rich apple heritage alive.

Ten South-western foods to try

Dittisham plum from the Dart valley, harvested in mid-August
Clotted cream
Cornish yarg a firm cow's milk cheese, wrapped in nettles
Bath chaps pig cheeks, boned, brined and cooked
Crabs
Gloucester Old Spot pig
Apple cake
Cornish pasty
Cider
Jersey royals in season April to June

What's good in October

Vegetables Beetroot * Borlotti bean (for podding) * Broccoli (Calabrese) * Cabbage (various green varieties) * Cardoon * Carrot * Cauliflower * Celeriac * Celery * Chard * Courgette * Fennel * Kale (and borecole) * Kohlrabi * Leek * Onion * Peppers and chillies * Potato * Pumpkin (and squash) * Rocket * Salsify (& scorzonera) * Spinach * Tomato * Turnip Fruit Apple, late (Egremont Russet, Blenheim Orange, Orleans Reinette) * Apple, store (Cox, Fiesta, Ashmead's Kernel, Bramley) * Damson * Grapes (English hothouse) * Medlars * Pear, late (Concorde, Doyenne du Comice, Conference, Winter Nellis) * Quince * Raspberries Wild greens and herbs Nettles * Watercress Wild flowers and fruits Bullace * Crab apple * Elderberries * Juniper berries * Rosehip * Rowan berries * Sloes Fungi and Nuts Chanterelle * Chestnut * Giant Puffball * Hedgehog fungus * Horse mushroom * Oyster mushroom (pleurotte) * Parasol * Shaggy Ink Cap * Summer Truffle * Walnut * Wood Blewit Fish and shellfish Cod * Crab (brown, hen and spider) * Eel * Lobster * Mackerel * Mussel * Oyster (native and rock) * Prawn * Scallop * Sea bass * Sprat * Squid * Trout, river (brown and rainbow) * Wild salmon Game Goose (wild) * Grey squirrel * Grouse * Hare * Mallard * Partridge * Rabbit * Snipe * Wood pigeon

Apple, beetroot and cheddar salad

Make a vinaigrette by mixing together *1 tbsp hempseed or olive oil*, *2 tbsp sunflower oil*, *1 tbsp cider vinegar* and a pinch each *salt*, *pepper* and *sugar*. Core and thinly slice *1 crisp eating apple*, such as Orleans Reinette. Peel and very thinly slice *1 small, raw beetroot* (about the same size as the apple). Use the vinaigrette to dress *3 good handfuls salad leaves*. Divide these between 2 dishes. Scatter the apple and beetroot over the leaves. Slice, then crumble *100g mature cheddar* and scatter this over too. Finish with *50g lightly toasted, skinned hazelnuts*. Serves 2.

Easy mushroom tart

Preheat the oven to 190°C/Gas Mark 5. Heat *25g butter* in a small pan and add *200g sliced mushrooms* and a pinch of *salt*. As the mushrooms soften, throw in *1 chopped clove garlic* and fry gently for another 2–3 minutes or so. You want the mushrooms to be tender and their liquid evaporated. Remove the pan from the heat and stir in *breadcrumbs made from 1 slice white bread*, the *grated zest of ½ lemon*, *1 heaped tbsp grated Parmesan*, *1 tbsp chopped parsley* and a few grinds of *black pepper*. Roll out *250g puff pastry* into a rough circle, no more than 5mm thick. Use this to line the base only of a 20cm diameter tart tin or ovenproof frying pan, and trim off the excess. Heap the mushroom mixture into the pastry, leaving a couple of centimetres uncovered around the edge. Brush this edge with *beaten egg* and bake for around 20 minutes, until the pastry is puffed up and golden. Serve hot or cold. Serves 2.

Wiltshire lardy cake

Stir *5g dried yeast* into *150ml warm water*. Set aside until frothy. Put *250g strong white bread flour* and a good pinch of *salt* in a bowl. Melt *10g lard* and set aside. Pour the yeast liquid and the melted lard into the flour and mix. Turn out and knead for 5–10 minutes until smooth and elastic then put in a clean bowl, cover and leave until doubled in size. Preheat the oven to 220°C/Gas Mark 7. Combine *50g sultanas*, *50g currants* and *50g chopped, candied peel* with *50g caster sugar* and *1 tsp ground cinnamon*. Cut *150g lard* into small dice. Knock back the dough and roll out to a rectangle. Scatter over half the dried fruit and lard, then roll it up. Give it a quarter turn and roll out again to a rectangle. Scatter over the remaining fruit and lard, roll up again, and roll out to fit a greased 20cm square, high-sided baking tin. Let the dough rise for another 30 minutes. Bake for 30–40 minutes until well risen and golden brown. Cool in the tin for 10–15 minutes before turning out. Leave the loaf upside down so the melted lard will be reabsorbed into the dough. Serve warm or cold. Serves 8.

6   **Monday**

7   **☽ Tuesday**

8   **Wednesday**

9   **Thursday**

Friday 10

Saturday 11

Sunday 12

Notes

October

13   **Monday**

14   ○ **Tuesday**

15   **Wednesday**

16   **Thursday**

Friday

17

Saturday

18

Sunday

19

Notes

October

20   **Monday**

21   ◑ **Tuesday**

22   **Wednesday**

23   **Thursday**

Friday

24

Saturday

25

Sunday

26

British Summertime ends

Notes

October

27   Monday

28   ● Tuesday

29   Wednesday

30   Thursday

November

Yorkshire and the Humber

Potto Grange Organics

Marian Rogers' family has been rearing pedigree livestock at Potto Grange for over 200 years. Her father introduced the rare White Galloway, an old native breed, and Marian's aim is to create a semi-wild herd with her own 50-strong herd. Calves are born outdoors in the springtime with little or no assistance, and suckle their mothers for as long as they wish. They grow up alongside their siblings, creating a strong family bond within the herd. Marian believes the ancient pasture they graze on supplies a wide variety of herbs, giving the cattle a chance to self-medicate as necessary. This results in an exceptionally healthy stock for which conventional medicines are rarely needed. White Galloways are a slow-maturing breed that produces a well-marbled, intensely flavoured beef. They are left for at least 30 months before going to slaughter, allowing them to put on weight naturally. Marian lets the meat to hang for 3–4 weeks, and then sells the organic beef from her farmhouse and at local farmers' markets.

Ten foods to try from Yorkshire

Champagne rhubarb available from late December to early April
Wilfra tart an apple and cheese tart
Fat Rascals large fruited tea cakes
Parkin a dark sticky ginger cake
Ribston Pippin a late-season dessert apple, harvested in late September
Dock pudding a purée of cooked nettles, sweet dock and other spring herbs
Swaledale cheese a lemony, buttery cheese made from ewe's or cow's milk
York ham
Yorkshire curd tart
Denby Dale pie stewed beef, covered with sliced potato and shortcrust pastry

What's good in November

Vegetables Artichoke (Jerusalem) * Beetroot * Brussels tops * Cabbage (red, white and various green varieties) * Cardoon * Carrot * Celeriac * Celery * Chard * Chicory * Endive * Greens (spring and winter) * Kale (and borecole) * Kohlrabi * Leek * Lettuce * Onion * Parsnip * Potato * Pumpkin (and squash) * Salsify (and scorzonera) * Swede * Turnip Fruit Apple, late (Egremont Russet, Blenheim Orange, Orleans Reinette) * Apple, store (Cox, Fiesta, Ashmead's Kernel, Bramley) * Medlars * Pear, late (Concorde, Doyenne du Comice, Conference, Winter Nellis) * Quince * Raspberries Wild greens and herbs Nettles * Watercress Wild flowers and fruits Rosehip * Sloes Fungi and Nuts Chestnut * Hedgehog fungus * Horse mushroom * Oyster mushroom (pleurotte) * Walnut * Wood Blewit Fish and shellfish Cod * Crab (brown, hen) * Lobster * Mackerel * Mussel * Oyster (native and rock) * Prawns * Scallop * Sea bass * Sprat * Squid * Whiting Game Goose (wild) * Grey squirrel * Grouse * Hare * Mallard * Partridge * Pheasant * Rabbit * Snipe * Wood pigeon

Roast rib of beef with fresh horseradish sauce

Preheat the oven to 220–230°C/Gas Mark 7–8. Massage a
4–5kg joint aged rib of beef with olive oil or soft dripping and season all
over with salt and pepper. Place in a roasting tin and put in the hot oven.
Cook for about 30 minutes, until browned and sizzling. Turn the oven down
to 180°C/Gas Mark 4. Then allow 10–12 minutes per 500g for very rare
meat, 14–15 minutes for rare, or 18–20 minutes for medium. Remove from
the oven, transfer to a warm serving plate and cover with foil. Leave to rest
for 30 minutes (your Yorkshire pud, see below, can go in to the oven now).
Meanwhile, peel and grate 100g fresh horseradish root, combine with
2 tsp cider vinegar, 1 tsp English mustard and a pinch of sugar. Leave
for 10 minutes. Stir in 125g crème fraiche, and season to taste. Carve the
beef thickly and serve with roast potatoes, seasonal veg, the horseradish
sauce and Yorkshire pud. Serves 10.

Yorkshire pudding

Put 250g plain flour, a good pinch of salt, 6 whole eggs, 2 egg whites and
600ml whole milk in a food processor. With the plunger removed to help
aeration, process in five 10-second bursts until you have a smooth batter.
Leave to rest for at least 30 minutes. Preheat the oven to 220°C/Gas Mark 7.
Put a knob of lard or 2 tbsp oil in a large roasting tin and put in the oven
for at least 5 minutes, until smoking. Making sure the oil is still smoking
hot (you can even put the tin on the hob to maintain the heat), pour in
the batter and return to the oven. Cook for 25–30 minutes, until the pud
is puffed up and a deep golden brown. Serve in thick slices. Serves 10.

Apple pie with Wensleydale

Combine 300g plain white flour with a pinch of salt. Rub in 150g cold,
diced butter until the mix resembles breadcrumbs, then add 1 egg yolk
and 2–3 tbsp ice cold water and bring the pastry together. Knead lightly,
then wrap and chill for 30 minutes. Preheat the oven to 200°C/Gas Mark
6. Peel, core and slice 1.5kg well-flavoured dessert apples, such as Ribston
Pippins. Roll out two-thirds of the pastry and use to line a deep, 25cm
diameter pie dish. Fill the pastry with the apple slices, sprinkling on
about 3 tbsp caster sugar and a few pinches of ground cinnamon as you
go. Brush the edge of the pastry with water. Roll out the remaining pastry
and top the pie. Crimp the edges and trim off the excess. Brush with beaten
egg, make a hole in the top for steam, and bake for about 45 minutes. Serve
hot, with a generous wedge of Wensleydale cheese on the side of each
portion. Serves 8.

Friday

31

Halloween

Saturday

1

Sunday

2

Notes

November

Week 44

3   **Monday**

4   **Tuesday**

5   **Wednesday**

6   **◐ Thursday**

Friday

7

Saturday

8

Bridport Farmers' Market

Sunday

9

Remembrance Sunday

Notes

November

10   Monday

11   Tuesday

12   Wednesday

13   ○ Thursday

Friday

14

Saturday

15

Sunday

16

Notes

November

17   Monday

18   Tuesday

19   ◑ Wednesday

20   Thursday

Friday   **21**

Saturday   **22**

Sunday   **23**

Notes

24   Monday

25   Tuesday

26   Wednesday

27   ● Thursday

Friday

28

Saturday

29

Sunday

30

St Andrew's Day

Notes

November

1   **Monday**

Welsh Winter Fair (www.rwas.co.uk), until Tuesday 2nd December

2   **Tuesday**

3   **Wednesday**

4   **Thursday**

December

The West Midlands

Goodman's free-range geese

When her family faced a gooseless Christmas in 1981, Judy Goodman decided she'd have to start raising her own birds on the family farm at Great Witley in Worcestershire. News of her enterprise quickly spread and her flock of a few hundred rapidly grew to a few thousand. Originally selling her geese from the farm gate, Judy became a pioneer of overnight meat delivery and soon her geese were being cooked up and down the land. The birds arrive on the farm in spring and early summer as day-old Legarth goslings. After a free-range life fuelled by a natural diet of grass and corn, they are ready to eat from September onwards. This is in keeping with the British tradition of serving goose at Michaelmas. An autumn goose is very different to a Christmas one, being much leaner – 'it hasn't put on its winter coat,' Judy explains. In recent years, she's added free-range bronze turkeys to her range, but she is still fondly known as 'the goose lady of Worcester'.

Ten foods to try from the West Midlands

Tamworth pig
Shropshire Blue cheese
Evesham asparagus ready 10–14 days ahead of the main crop in the East of Britain
Worcester Pearmain a sweet, juicy, early-season dessert apple
Blackcurrants
Pershore plum a yellow plum, excellent for cooking
Hereford Hops cheese cow's milk cheese coated with hops
Staffordshire oat cake a substantial type of pancake
Hereford cider brandy
Perry

What's good in December

Vegetables Artichoke (Jerusalem) * Brussels sprouts * Brussels tops * Cabbage (red, white and various green varieties) * Carrot * Celeriac * Celery * Chicory * Endive * Greens (spring and winter) * Kale (and borecole) * Leek * Lettuce * Onion * Parsnip * Potato * Swede * Turnip Fruit Apple, late (Egremont Russet, Blenheim Orange, Orleans Reinette) * Apple, store (Cox, Fiesta, Ashmead's Kernel, Bramley) * Rhubarb (forced) Fungi and Nuts Chestnut Fish and shellfish Cod * Crab (brown, hen) * Mussels * Oyster (native and rock) * Sea bass * Whiting Game Goose (farmed and wild) * Grey squirrel * Grouse * Hare * Mallard * Partridge * Pheasant * Snipe * Woodcock * Wood pigeon

Mini kebabs of goose, apple and chestnut

Preheat the oven to 190°C/Gas Mark 5. Stretch *8 rashers smoked, streaky bacon* with the back of a knife, then cut each rasher into three lengths. Core *3 crisp eating apples* (such as Cox or Worcester Pearmain) and cut each into 8 wedges. Cut *250g goose meat* into chunky cubes. You'll also need *24 whole, cooked, peeled chestnuts.* Wrap each chestnut, slice of apple and chunk of goose in a piece of bacon, and thread one of each onto a cocktail stick, snuggling them up close together. Alternatively, use thin wooden skewers. Place in an ovenproof dish and roast for 20 minutes until the bacon is crisp. Serve hot, with napkins. Makes 24.

Shropshire Blue and parsnip soup

Heat *25g butter* in a large saucepan. Add *1 chopped onion* and *1 chopped stem celery*, season lightly and sweat over a low heat for 10–15 minutes until soft. Add *500g peeled, diced parsnip* and sweat for a few minutes more, then pour on *1.2 litres vegetable or chicken stock*. Bring to a simmer and cook gently until the parsnip is completely tender. Liquidise the soup, then return to the pan and reheat gently – don't let it boil. Add *200g crumbled Shropshire Blue cheese* and stir until melted. Taste and season again if necessary, then serve in warmed bowls with a good scattering of black pepper on top. Serves 4–6.

Pikelets

Stir *5g dried yeast* into *250ml warm milk* and set aside until frothy. Sieve *250g plain flour* and a good pinch of *salt* into a bowl and make a well in the centre. Add *2 beaten eggs* and the warm yeast mixture and beat until you have a smooth batter the consistency of double cream. Set aside for about an hour to rise. Heat a flat griddle or a large, non-stick frying pan over a medium heat until hot, then grease it with a smear of *oil*. Drop tablespoonfuls of the batter on to the hot surface, leaving plenty of room for them to spread (you'll have to cook them in batches). Flip the pikelets after a couple of minutes and cook the second side for a minute or so more. Serve hot with butter. Makes 10–12.

Friday ◖

5

Bonfire Night

Saturday

6

Sunday

7

Notes

December

8 Monday

9 Tuesday

10 Wednesday

11 Thursday

Friday ○   **12**

Saturday   **13**

Bridport Farmers' Market

Sunday   **14**

Notes

December

15 Monday

16 Tuesday

17 Wednesday

18 Thursday

Friday ☽

19

Saturday

20

Sunday

21

Winter Solstice

Notes

December

22

23

Tuesday

24

Wednesday

25

Thursday

Christmas Day

Friday

26

Saturday ●

27

Sunday

28

Notes

December

29 Monday

30 Tuesday

31 Wednesday

1 Thursday

Friday

2

Saturday

3

Sunday

4

Notes

January

Get in touch...

Axminster

River Cottage Store / Trinity Square / Axminster / Devon / EX13 5AN /
01297 631715 / rivercottage.net

Thyme after Time / Glue Hill / Sturminster Newton / Dorset / DT10 2DH /
01258 471911 / thymeaftertime.co.uk

Brown Cow Organics / organics@browncoworganics.co.uk /
browncoworganics.co.uk

Brown and Forrest / Bowdens Farm / Hambridge / Somerset / TA10 0BP /
01458 250875 / info@smokedeel.co.uk / smokedeel.co.uk

The Town Mill Bakery / Mill Lane / Lyme Regis / DT7 3PU / 01297 443579 /
info@townmillbakery.co.uk / townmillbakery.co.uk

Sydling Brook Farm / Sydling St Nicholas / Dorchester / Dorset / DT2 9PQ /
01300 341992 / sydling.co.uk

Roskilly's of Cornwall / Tregellast Barton / St Keverne / Helston / Cornwall /
TR12 6NX / 01326 280479 / roskillys.co.uk

January

Swallowfish Limited / Fisherman's Kitchen / 2 South Street / Seahouses /
NE68 7RB / 01665 721052 / info@swallowfish.co.uk / swallowfish.co.uk

February

Richard Haward / The Company Shed / 129 Coast Road /
West Mersea / Colchester / Essex / CO5 8PA / 01206 383284 /
enquiries@richardhawardsoysters.co.uk / richardhawardsoysters.co.uk

March

O'Doherty's Fine Meats / Belmore Street / Enniskillen / Co Fermanagh /
02866 322152 / sales@blackbacon.com / blackbacon.com

April

Ram Hall Farm / Berkswell / West Midlands / CV7 7BD / 01676 532203 /
berkswell@ram-hall.co.uk / sheepscheese.com

...with the producers featured in this year's diary

May

Growing Communities / The Old Fire Station / 61 Leswin Road /
Stoke Newington / London / N16 7NY / 020 7502 7588 /
growcomm@growingcommunities.org / www.growingcommunities.org

The Stoke Newington Farmers' Market takes place at William Patten
School, Stoke Newington Church Street, London N16, every Saturday
(except Christmas and New Year) from 10am until 2.30pm.

June

Graig Farm Organics / Dalau / Llandrindod Wells / Powys / LD1 5TL /
01597 851655 / sales@graigfarm.co.uk / graigfarm.co.uk

July

Park Farm Cherry Orchard / Lynsted Lane / Lynsted /
info@lynsted-orchard.org.uk / lynsted-orchard.org.uk

August

John Mellis / Cleuch House / Auldgirth / Dumfries / DG2 OTP /
01848 331280

September

Steve Pymm / Cumbria Wild Game / Brooklyn / Matterdale End / Penrith /
Cumbria / CA11 0LF / 01768 482503 / PymmB@aol.com / tasteofthelakes.com

October

Orchard Link / PO Box 109 / Totnes / Devon / TQ9 5XR / 07792 664710 /
info@orchardlink.org.uk / orchardlink.org.uk

November

Marian Rogers / Potto Grange Organics / Potto Grange / Potto /
Northallerton / North Yorkshire / DL6 3HH / 01642 700646 /
pottogrange.co.uk

December

Goodman's Geese / Walsgrove Farm / Great Witley / Worcestershire /
WR6 6JJ / 01299 896272 / sales@goodmansgeese.co.uk /
goodmansgeese.co.uk

Addresses

Name

Address

Telephone   Mobile

Email

Name

Address

Telephone   Mobile

Email

Name

Address

Telephone   Mobile

Email

Name

Address

Telephone   Mobile

Email

Name
_____

Address
_____

_____

Telephone   Mobile
_____

Email
_____

Name
_____

Address
_____

_____

Telephone   Mobile
_____

Email
_____

Name
_____

Address
_____

_____

Telephone   Mobile
_____

Email
_____

Name
_____

Address
_____

_____

Telephone   Mobile
_____

Email
_____

Name
_____

Address
_____

_____

Telephone   Mobile
_____

Email
_____

Name

Address

Telephone   Mobile

Email

Name

Address

Telephone   Mobile

Email

Name

Address

Telephone   Mobile

Email

Name

Address

Telephone   Mobile

Email

Name

Address

Telephone   Mobile

Email

Name

Address

Telephone   Mobile

Email

Name

Address

Telephone   Mobile

Email

Name

Address

Telephone   Mobile

Email

Name

Address

Telephone   Mobile

Email

Name

Address

Telephone   Mobile

Email

Name

Address

Telephone   Mobile

Email

Name

Address

Telephone   Mobile

Email

Name

Address

Telephone   Mobile

Email

Name

Address

Telephone   Mobile

Email

Name

Address

Telephone   Mobile

Email